OUT OF

When tragedy struck him, Fabian
Blackthorne was forced to rely more
and more on Cathy Milner—and Cathy
didn't mind at all. But was it much
consolation to know that, in any other
circumstances, he would only want
Cerise Hunniford?

OUT OF THIS DARKNESS

BY

MADELEINE KER

MILLS & BOON LIMITED

15–16 BROOK'S MEWS
LONDON W1A 1DR

First published 1984
Australian copyright 1984
Philippine copyright 1984
This edition 1984

© Madeleine Ker 1984

ISBN 0 263 74835 9

Set in Monophoto Times 10 on 10 pt.
01-1184 – 60621

*Made and printed in Great Britain by
Richard Clay (The Chaucer Press) Ltd,
Bungay, Suffolk*

CHAPTER ONE

CATHY could place all the furnishings in the lawyer's waiting-room at a glance. Her practised eye read Sanderson, Charles Hammond, Grant International. Businesslike but elegant. She could even hazard a guess at which antique shop had supplied the Georgian desk upon which the indifferent blonde secretary was typing an immaculate hundred words a minute with immaculately manicured fingers. Small comfort.

The tautness of her anxiety was an ache. She knew it was evident in every line of her body, in the way she was sitting, with her knees pressed together, her back rigid with tension. She didn't dare relax, though, in case the pent-up tears spilled right over, destroying the fragile balance she'd spent so many hours building up.

The immaculate blonde secretary, Cathy guessed, was well used to pale-faced clients sitting rigid in this office, waiting for ominous interviews. Though her family had used the legal firm of Morningstar, Blackthorne and Associates for well over fifty years, she herself had never set foot in the office before, had never anticipated that she would. She opened her clenched fist, and studied the lines her nails had made in her palm.

A green light winked on, and the secretary rose on slender legs.

'Mr Blackthorne will see you now,' she decided. She ushered Cathy to a panelled doorway. 'It's Mr Fabian Blackthorne you're seeing, Miss Milner. The senior partner's son. Will that be all right?'

'Oh!' Cathy paused unhappily. 'Isn't Keith Blackthorne free?'

'I'm afraid he's still in court at the moment. He probably won't be back today.'

'Oh.' Cathy's heart sank even further as the image of Keith Blackthorne, a kindly old man who had been a lifelong adviser to her father, receded. Hand on the doorknob, the secretary studied Cathy's pale face. 'Fabian Blackthorne is extremely capable,' she said gently. 'But if you can wait until tomorrow——'

'No,' Cathy said, shaking her head quickly. Her business was much too urgent for that. 'I'll see his son now.'

'Go straight through, then.'

Fabian Blackthorne rose to meet her as she walked uncertainly into his office. He was an intimidatingly tall man. The dark, conservative suit he wore had been tailored as though to disguise the raw and dangerous power of his body. A panther, Cathy thought instinctively, in Savile Row clothing. And despite his polite smile, his eyes were North-Sea-cold. She felt her own eyes wince away from the attack of that dispassionate grey gaze, and her mind dissolved into blankness. He looked so aloof, so cold! How was she ever going to be able to confide in this man? Not for the first time, it occurred to her that she should have sought out a woman lawyer.

His handshake was brief. 'Please sit down, Miss Milner,' he said in a deep voice. 'We haven't met before, have we?'

'No, I d-don't think so.'

'I was very sorry to hear about your father's heart attack. I trust his health is improving?'

'Yes, it is. But I—I haven't come on family business,' Cathy blurted out hastily. She sat down, trying not to quail under the level stare. 'And I want you to promise that you'll never tell my father that I came to see you. Please!'

'I see,' said Fabian Blackthorne. He leaned back in his chair, thoughtful eyes studying Cathy from under dark, curved brows. 'Everything between a lawyer and his client is always in the strictest confidence, Miss Milner. Always. Is this a question of money?'

'Money?' Cathy echoed. Surprise almost made her smile. 'Nothing as easy as that!' He pulled a note-pad towards him, waiting. Though the handsome face didn't register it, she could sense the lawyer's curiosity. Up till now, she realised, his firm's dealings with her family had been strictly orthodox. The Milners were by no means hugely wealthy; but they had been producing competent soldiers, civil servants, politicians and scholars for generations. The seamier side of life had probably never even been acknowledged.

Until now, she thought bitterly.

'I'm in trouble, Mr Blackthorne.' Unconsciously, her fingers were fretting together, her right thumb rubbing at the place on her left hand where a ring had once glittered. The memory of what she had done loomed up like a nightmare, paralysing her. 'The thing is that I—I don't know how to explain it all . . .'

She could see lines gathering wearily around his eyes. 'Very well,' he said drily. 'Have you killed anyone?'

'Oh no,' Cathy grimaced. 'Nothing like that.' She looked uncertainly into the hard-chiselled features. 'I want you to get something back for me.'

'I see.' Polite but distinctly cool now, Mr Blackthorne surveyed her across an expanse of red Morocco leather. The deep grey eyes hadn't missed her preoccupation with her naked engagement finger. 'What sort of something, Miss Milner? Jewellery? Letters?'

'Some photographs,' she said.

'Photographs of whom?'

'Of me.' Her mouth opened to tell him what kind of photographs, but she just couldn't. She remembered the sickening heat of the arc-lights, the unwinking glass eye of the camera, and her throat contracted, choking the words.

'Who took these photographs?' he asked patiently, trying to ease her confession. She could feel her colour ebbing fast.

'I don't know his name.' She drew a shaky breath, trying to ease that strange tightness in her throat. 'A professional photographer. He—he works for a magazine called *Caprice*.' She stopped there, on the brink of calling off the whole thing. How in God's name was she going to explain what she'd done to him, when she couldn't even explain it to herself?

'I don't think I've heard of it,' Mr Blackthorne probed quietly, and paused for Cathy to enlighten him. 'If you don't take me into your confidence, Miss Milner, I can do nothing for you. You do understand that?' She nodded, plucking at the lilac silk of her dress, and tried to gulp down tears. She didn't want to cry, and it was an exhausting effort not to just melt, right here in this immaculate office in front of this immaculately-dressed man.

But her muteness was obviously irritating Fabian Blackthorne, because he sighed quietly, and glanced at the slim gold Cartier on his wrist.

'They're studio pictures,' she blurted out. 'I—I went to the *Caprice* studio for a modelling session and——'

'Fashion pictures?' he asked as she ground to halt. 'What are you wearing in the photographs?'

'A red straw hat,' she said. Her voice was almost inaudible, and Fabian Blackthorne's black eyebrows came down in puzzlement as he scribbled in his pad.

'A what—a red straw hat?'

'Yes.'

'What else?'

There was a heavy silence. He looked up sharply, thick dark lashes narrowing his piercing gaze.

'You mean—a red straw hat, and nothing else?'

'Yes,' she said. Or rather, her lips formed the word, but no sound came out. His glance raked over her, from the soft cloud of her raven-dark hair to her neat grey court shoes.

'You posed in the nude?' he queried. Cathy nodded silently, her face turned away. 'Are the pictures pornographic?'

The word was horrible to her. 'No,' she whispered, 'I—I don't think so.'

'What they call "artistic", then?'

'I—I suppose so.' She thought for a few seconds. 'The photographer had a machine that made smoke . . . a sort of foggy effect.' She could still smell the stuff in her nostrils. 'I don't really know what the pictures are like.'

'You don't seem to know much,' he said shortly. 'I take it that *Caprice* is one of the glossy confections that pass as "adult" reading—lots of nudes and articles on how to improve your sex life?'

'I think it's something like that,' Cathy nodded miserably.

He shook his head slowly. 'And now you want out— is that right?'

'Yes.' Having made the confession, she felt marginally better. What Fabian Blackthorne was thinking of her, though, she dreaded to think. 'Can you help me?' she pleaded.

'I'm not sure,' he admitted thoughtfully. He was watching her with an odd expression. 'I take it they made you sign a model release? And gave you a fee?'

'Five hundred pounds,' she said. 'I tore the cheque up.'

'Have you got a copy of the contract?'

Silently, avoiding his eyes, she passed the document over to him. He studied it, his mouth set in a grim line.

'What in God's name made you do something as idiotic as this?' he asked, almost to himself.

'That's my business,' she said tersely, her raw nerves reacting with sudden anger.

'Are they going to use your name with the pictures?' he asked, watching the expression of rebellious bitterness settle on her face.

'They'll use my first name,' she replied dully. The photographer had told her so as she'd dressed, sick and shaking, behind the screen. *Lovely pictures*, he'd said. *Come back again soon—you're a natural.*

'Ah.' He surveyed her expressionlessly, then picked up the discreet ebony telephone beside him. 'Melanie? Get me *Caprice* magazine, please—London N5.'

There was a silence as he waited for the connection. Cathy found herself studying his hands with the odd clarity that emotional strain sometimes brings. Good, strong hands, with tapering fingers ... No amount of Savile Row silk could quite sheathe the raw, almost blade-like quality of this man. What would he be thinking of her now, what distaste was his cold face concealing? The lashes over his downcast eyes were long for a man, adding an almost exotic hint to the ruthlessly male features.

The conversation which Fabian Blackthorne had with the person at the other end was deceptively calm and friendly. Unaware of Cathy's troubled gaze on his face, he set about finding what he wanted, making quick, neat notes as he listened and talked. Her restless brain wouldn't let her follow the conversation properly, but she flinched as the receiver clicked down again.

'That was a lady called Cerise Hunniford.' His tanned face was even more thoughtful as he turned back to Cathy. 'Apparently she's the editor of *Caprice* magazine—and, it seems, of half a dozen other magazines operating under the same company's banner.'

'Did you find out about the pictures?' she asked.

'*Caprice* has a circulation of three hundred thousand,' he said bluntly. 'And rising. You're scheduled for the centrefold of the August issue, two months from now.' His dark, arching eyebrows descended, giving him a formidable look. 'Do I need to spell out what this will do to your reputation? And what your father will go through?'

'No,' she said through gritted teeth. 'I haven't had much else on my mind for the past week.' Defiance and despair struggled in her. How could he understand? 'What did that woman say?'

'She said,' Fabian Blackthorne answered calmly, his eyes holding hers, 'that you're one of the best models they've had. "Young and very classy", were her words.' He tapped his pen slowly on the desk. 'She also told me that you came into the studio and asked one of her photographers directly for a modelling session there and then. Apparently, you were eager to bare your soul for the cameras. "Amateur but very co-operative", according to Ms Hunniford.'

Cathy squeezed her eyes shut, nails cutting into her palms as the horrible scene rose up before her. The heat of the spotlights. The alcohol numbing her brain. The swirls of artificial mist, designed to add the barest hint of modesty to the session.

And the anger that blazed in her veins, the almost wild desire to hurt, to destroy, to revenge ... Anger that had taught her to smile with seductive red lips. Anger like a rowel in the flesh of her mind, urging her to thrust out her breasts, arch her neck, look back over her naked shoulder with cheap, animal sensuality at the unwinking eye of the camera.

And the photographer's voice behind the dazzling lights, 'Lovely, darling—hold it just there—okay, arms back—lovely, love-*lee*!'

And then the growing sanity that sent her shivering for her clothes. The numbed, shaking drive home. And vomiting into the basin with sickened heart and splitting head. And the week of black depression, of self-disgust that had followed.

Slowly she raised her white face and opened aching eyes to face the lawyer. Who are you to judge? she thought bitterly. What the hell do you know about betrayal, about disillusionment?

'I didn't enjoy it, Mr Blackthorne,' she said, her voice low but steady. 'No one enjoys being degraded.'

'No.' But Mr Blackthorne's face wasn't wearing sympathy either. 'There's no guarantee we can get those pictures back, Miss Milner. It's not their policy to withdraw material to suit a model's whims. "They all get cold feet just before publication." That's another quote from the capable Ms Hunniford. Once a model's signed a contract, that's that as far as they're concerned.'

'I see,' Cathy said tiredly. The red of her lipstick was the only splash of colour in her face now. Even her emerald-green eyes, making such a striking contrast to her black hair, seemed pale and muted by pain. At least he had said 'we'. She sighed. 'But you're going to try?'

'Yes. You and I are going to meet Ms Hunniford this afternoon.' He caught her expression of dismay. 'You've tangled yourself in a very rough contract, Miss

Milner. This isn't going to be easy. If you'll take my advice, you'll tell your father the whole story right now——'

'*No!*' The word was almost torn from her throat. 'No,' she repeated more calmly. 'Never. This would kill Daddy. You know that he isn't well. I couldn't hurt him like this——'

'He'll be even more hurt if we can't persuade Ms Hunniford to withdraw those pictures,' Fabian Blackthorne said grimly. 'You puzzle me, Miss Milner.' His dark eyes searched her face and figure again, noting the beautiful, simple lines of her clothes, the exquisite taste of her jewellery. 'You're not the sort of person who behaves like this. I find it very hard to imagine you in a red straw hat.' He ran his hand through thick, dark hair. 'Why did you do it? Maybe if you told me the background to this crazy story we'd find some way out.'

'I don't think you'd understand, Mr Blackthorne,' she replied wearily. 'And I don't feel like talking about it. If you can't get those pictures back——' She broke off, biting her lip.

'You'll do something even more stupid? Like killing yourself?' He shook his head with ice-cold eyes. 'Nothing's that easy, Miss Milner,' he growled. 'If you'll forgive me for saying so, you've obviously led a pampered life. Well, now you've got yourself into a mess, and I'm afraid you're just going to have to sit tight.' More gently, he went on, 'Look, I'm going to do my best. There are very strong links between this firm and your family, and the last thing I want is to see any harm come to you personally. I repeat my advice—tell your father. Or even your mother. She's in France now, isn't she?'

'Spain,' Cathy said dully. 'I couldn't tell either of them, believe me.'

'As you please.' He rose to his feet. 'Our appointment's at three this afternoon. And yes,' he went on, cutting through what she was about to say, 'you *do* have to be there. I warn you this may cost something.'

'Anything,' she whispered, rising on shaky legs. 'I'll sell everything I've got if necessary——'

'We'll see what happens,' he interrupted. The dark grey eyes, with their inner hint of stormy sea, seemed to warm for a second. 'Try not to upset yourself any further, Cathy. I'll meet you in this office at, shall we say two-thirty?'

His handshake was warm and strong. Oddly, it left a faint trace of warmth in the cold of her soul as she walked blindly through the opulent reception room outside, past the immaculate secretary, whose immaculate, well-groomed mind, she thought with bitter envy, held not a trace of pain or despair.

'You still don't want to tell me *why* you did this crazy thing?'

'No,' Cathy said tensely. He took her arm as they crossed the busy street, and somehow the touch of his hand jarred on her strained nerves.

'No matter.' They stopped at the doorway of the *Caprice* building. The sight of it had already sent the miserable memories whirling through Cathy's mind. When you've just been hurt, hurt and betrayed in the most horrible way, you *do* do crazy things. Even things like posing for nude photographs. Fabian Blackthorne, big, self-confident and invulnerable, was never going to understand that. 'I want you to remember two things,' he said to her, staring hard into her eyes. 'Say as little as possible once we're in there—and trust me, whatever happens. Got that?'

'Yes,' she said.

'Okay, let's go and meet Cerise Hunniford.'

Cerise Hunniford was waiting for them in the penthouse suite. She was thirtyish, petite, redheaded—and she worked hard at being sexy. Her clinging black blouse set off her smooth, tanned skin perfectly, adding glitter to the blue eyes, and making the wide red mouth seem even brighter. A formidable and formidably attractive woman, Cathy thought with a sinking heart, and not one to play games with.

She ushered them to comfortable chairs in front of her vast, spotlessly neat desk, and lit a cigarette with a slim gold lighter.

'You look surprised, Mr Blackthorne,' she drawled through a cloud of Turkish smoke. 'Didn't you expect to find a woman at the head of a big company?'

'I didn't expect to find a woman in command of an enterprise like this one,' he admitted. Cathy glanced around the sleek, ultra-modern office. The buttermilk-yellow walls were decorated with block-mounted covers from Aphrodite's many publications—*Caprice*, *Dreamgirls*, *Adam's Domain*, *Rascals* ... Crimson lips and sultry eyes, hints of expensively presented and glamorous sex within. A cleverly organised array of glossy, pricey magazines that kept perfect pace between what was chic and fashionable, and what was frankly erotic.

Cerise Hunniford followed Cathy's gaze with catlike mascaraed eyes.

'You disapprove? That's not very liberated of you, Miss Milner. You made a wise choice in coming to *Caprice*, believe me. Glamour sells very well, especially when it's spiced with a little raw sex in the name of intellectual liberation—and we pay our models well.'

Cathy didn't reply to the subtly barbed taunt.

'You seem to be doing well on the mixture,' Fabian Blackthorne said coolly. 'Your product seems a street ahead of the average glamour magazine.'

'We like to think it's several blocks ahead,' Cerise Hunniford said with a brilliant smile. Her thirty-odd years of life had added an alluring sensuality to a face already made beautiful by nature. Looking at her trim, provocatively dressed figure, Cathy guessed at hours of squash, saunas and massage. Three or four holidays a year in exotic locations. And, naturally, a steady supply of expert lovers. She glanced quickly at Fabian Blackthorne's impassive face. Was he finding this woman desirable? The thought angered her, but she bit her feelings down. Her role, he had commanded, was to say as little as possible, and that was what she was going to do. 'Aphrodite is one of this country's leading publishers,' the other woman went on. 'Over the past five years, I've changed the face of glamour magazines in this country. I have nothing to be ashamed of.'

'I'm not criticising you,' Fabian reminded her calmly.

'Maybe you just have that sort of face,' Cerise Hunniford purred. She exhaled smoke through a deliberately open mouth like the muzzle of a gun. Her eyes lingered on Fabian Blackthorne's body, then moved up to his face, unperturbed by the hard challenge in his eyes. Cathy squirmed furiously in her chair. Having to sit and watch this creature flirt with Fabian was a kind of horrible torture. It was all she could do to remember his *trust me*. Cerise's sharp eyes didn't miss her slight movement, and she turned to Cathy. Her smile was mocking, slow, a fuse burning towards dynamite. 'You think me disgusting, Miss Milner?'

'You're a very clever woman,' Cathy replied tautly, the first words she had spoken so far. She tried to keep her face expressionless. 'I don't think you really give a damn what people think of you.'

'I don't. A drink, Miss Milner? Mr Blackthorne? I usually have a Pimm's at this time of the afternoon.' She rose to extract a ready-made drink from the refrigerator that had been designed to blend smoothly in with the décor of her office, giving them the benefit of her catlike walk as she did so. 'I've discovered that men like to dream about the impossible, every bit as much as women do.' She waved at the covers on the walls. 'I simply add a little substance to their dreams. The world is full of people making fools of themselves over sex, you know. Why shouldn't I cash in on that?' She sat down with lithe grace. 'My magazines bring colour into a great many drab lives. Aphrodite has a current readership of around the quarter million mark. When that gets to a million, I'll sell the business and retire to the Bahamas.'

'A very commendable ambition,' said Fabian. He looked swiftly at Cathy's pale, strained face, as though warning her to keep her temper—and her silence. 'Miss Hunniford, can we get down to the subject of Catherine Milner?'

'Ah—the daring Miss Milner.' Gold bangles clinked as Cerise raised the dew-beaded glass to her lips. Her eyes flickered between Cathy and the lawyer, as though trying to assess the exact relationship between them.

'This isn't an ordinary request to hold publication. My client is desperately unhappy about what's happened, and it's my considered opinion that if the photographs are printed, the effect on her health will be catastrophic.'

'Yes?' The voice was indifferent.

'Yes,' he replied emphatically. 'Catherine isn't a model, as you know. She belongs to a very old-established family. A family, I might add, who have given this country some very gallant soldiers in two world wars, and several gifted public servants. Catherine's father, as I'm sure you've heard, is the Member of Parliament for Northwood.'

'Patriotism,' purred Cerise, 'is the last refuge of scoundrels. So I've heard.' Cathy felt her face redden at the insult; yet she almost welcomed the anger uncurling inside her; it was a healthy antidote, she was discovering, to fear and despair. Fabian went on calmly, as though armour-plated by experience.

'Why she went through that photographic session is a mystery,' he confessed. He didn't look at Cathy. 'That isn't our business. It was, however, certainly an aberration of some kind—a very big mistake.'

'Girls from the highest families in this country have graced my covers from time to time,' Cerise Hunniford shrugged. 'And if you want a motivation, take vanity. Vanity happens to be a very powerful human impulse,' she said coolly. Her eyes flicked to Cathy. 'And it works most dramatically in young and pretty girls.'

'I don't think Catherine Milner came to you out of vanity,' Fabian Blackthorne disagreed courteously. 'And publishing those pictures won't do either the Milner family or your company any good at all.'

'No?' Slender eyebrows arched at him. 'You aren't trying to threaten me, Mr Blackthorne?'

'I'm merely stating the obvious,' he shrugged.

'It's not obvious to me,' Cerise Hunniford smiled sweetly. The sparkle in her eyes betrayed the enjoyment, even excitement, she was deriving from this interview. 'Withdrawing those pictures at this stage will cost me a lot of money and time.'

'How much money?' Fabian asked quietly.

'You're offering to pay?' Cerise's eyes were diamond-bright as she sipped at her Pimm's again. 'Okay. Five thousand pounds.'

'That's an absurd sum,' he retorted, his eyes cold and angry now.

The publisher leaned back in her chair, not bothering to disguise her amusement, and it occurred to Cathy, rather sickly, that she was enjoying his anger as though it were strong wine.

'I think it's fair. Miss Catherine Milner happens to be a very attractive and classy young lady. Readers are going to be queuing up to buy that edition.' She smiled sweetly at Cathy, then opened a drawer, and took out a large manila envelope. 'As a matter of fact, the pictures are really very good. I had them brought up to my office just before you came. Take a look.'

Cathy stared at the envelope in fascinated horror.

'No, thank you,' said Fabian, his jaw clenched with anger.

'Go on—they're very artistic.' Her smile embraced them both. 'Miss Milner has a truly delicious figure. Quite the most fabulous legs I've seen in a long time.'

'No, thank you,' he growled again, and Cathy caught the bleak fury in his eyes. With a woman's quick instinct, she knew what Fabian could never guess—that Cerise Hunniford was taking a great deal of sensual pleasure in needling his anger. The thought was profoundly depressing.

'Would it be so unprofessional to take a peek?' Cerise sighed. 'I suppose it might be.' She smiled blandly at Cathy. 'How about you, Miss Milner?'

'I don't want to look at them, no,' Cathy said quietly. 'I just want them back. Permanently. I *must* have them. I'm fully prepared to pay whatever you ask for them— or to go to any legal lengths if you won't sell.' The calm strength in her own words surprised her, and the petite woman behind the desk narrowed her eyes thoughtfully.

'Not just a pretty face, eh? Yes, I can see exactly the sort of class you come from. You do that superior, crushing tone so perfectly. I don't suppose you've ever worked for a living, *Miss* Milner?'

'As a matter of fact I have,' Cathy said shortly. 'That has nothing to do with this, though.'

Cerise looked at Fabian, her eyes watching him with new caution. 'May I call you Fabian? Fabian, people of Catherine Milner's class and type don't impress me. She was born with a silver spoon in her mouth. I clawed my way up from a family of ten in a council house in Canning Town. Why should I care what happens to her? Why shouldn't she be left to squeal? It might teach her a valuable lesson.'

'It might also damage her father's health seriously,' Fabian pointed out coolly, his dark brows coming down over storm-grey eyes. 'And it would certainly precipitate a crisis for Cathy herself.'

'You're quite sentimental about the divine Miss Milner, Mr Blackthorne,' the publisher sneered. 'Do tell—is there an attachment in the offing?'

To Cathy's surprise, the lawyer smiled suddenly. 'I don't want to interfere with your amusement, Ms Hunniford. It's pleasant to watch you having fun, and I've always heard that it's unwise to take a mouse away from a cat.'

'A charming simile.'

'But I don't play mouse to anyone's cat, I'm afraid.' His smile faded like the sun on a wintry day. 'I advise you not to make the mistake of underestimating me. You would regret it for a long time.'

'Yes?' The publisher tried to smile into those arctic eyes, but suddenly the edge of her amusement seemed to have been taken away.

'Oh, yes. I have power at my disposal. You may be big news in the publishing industry, but you're vulnerable. And if you choose to publish those pictures, I guarantee to make you repent of it. You may even have to postpone that retirement to the Bahamas for several years.'

'You mean you'd sue?'

'I mean you may find yourself facing prosecutions under the Obscene Publications Act,' he said flatly. 'You may find staying on the right side of the law rather more difficult from now on. I can also bring a not inconsiderable influence to bear on various people with whom you have to do business. And yes, I would definitely advise my client to sue you.'

Cathy found herself suddenly breathless at the cool menace in Fabian Blackthorne's voice.

'Now you *are* threatening me,' Cerise Hunniford said thoughtfully, toying with her glass.

'Yes.'

'*Caprice* isn't the Book of the Damned,' she complained irrelevantly. 'People have such lurid ideas about my magazines. The pictures aren't even all that revealing—there are wreaths of Scotch mist to keep things pure. I like to keep my readers hungry.'

'Miss Hunniford, we didn't come here to discuss the merits of your publications.' He glanced at his watch. 'We don't have too much time. Are you prepared to talk business or not?'

'Why don't we discuss the whole thing more comfortably?' Cerise Hunniford parried. She smiled sweetly, knotting a tendril of flame-red hair around one finger. 'Without the benefit of Miss Milner's company? Shall we say Thursday night, at Claridges?'

Cathy barely had time to swallow her instinctive anger before Fabian shrugged, and rose in one fluid movement. 'You're still playing games. I did warn you, didn't I?' Cathy rose with him, her heart thudding now. Had they failed? He nodded coolly at Cerise. 'Goodbye, Ms Hunniford. You'll be hearing from me.'

The publisher's catlike face twisted suddenly into a

sour smile. 'All right, Mr Blackthorne, you've made your point.'

'You agree to give up the photographs?' he asked calmly.

'For a price.' She drained her glass, her eyes cynical as she watched Cathy sink back into her chair, pale with relief. 'I hope you realise this is interference with the freedom of the press. Now, what exactly do you want from me?'

'A written undertaking not to print any photographs of my client whatsoever,' Fabian replied concisely. 'That means from now until Doomsday. Secondly, I want you to hand over all photographs, negatives or transparencies of my client in your possession.'

Cerise laughed shortly. 'You don't want much, Mr Blackthorne!'

'Do you agree to those terms?' he pressed. Cathy held her breath.

'If I must,' she shrugged. Her eyes spat anger at Cathy as she caught Cathy's little gasp of relief, but she kept her smile in place. 'In return, Mr Blackthorne, I want my five thousand. In cash.'

'That will have to be discussed,' he said calmly, his tone brooking no argument. 'Frankly, I doubt whether you'll get anything like that sum.'

'Then you can go to hell!' the petite woman retorted, her body rigid with anger.

'There's one last thing.' Fabian Blackthorne opened his briefcase and slid a document across the desk towards the publisher. 'That's an injunction forbidding you from printing anything about my client for the next three months. Disobey it at your peril, Ms Hunniford. It *is* renewable, so prepare to be reasonable. And I'll get back to you very shortly to discuss the question of money.'

'How did you get this?' Cerise said tensely, reading through the document.

'I told you I wasn't without influence. And I take my work seriously.' The dark strength of his face was lit by a slight smile suddenly. 'Good afternoon, Ms Hunniford. We'll be in touch.'

He rose, and took Cathy's arm in a strong hand, as though aware that she was in danger of stumbling on legs that suddenly felt like wet spaghetti, and walked her through the doorway towards the lift. He didn't bother to glance back at Cerise Hunniford. In the chromed cell of the lift, he gave her a dry look.

'I hope you weren't upset by any of that stuff about your background,' he said.

'No,' she replied, still slightly stunned by the outcome of this afternoon's interview. 'People always imagine that my family is immensely rich—it's actually rather poor. But I went to my local comprehensive, Mr Blackthorne—I got used to being teased. And I long ago realised I didn't have to be ashamed of having a father who's a baronet.'

'Good. Where do you work, as a matter of interest?'

'I'm Kaspar Aprahamian's personal assistant,' she told him, feeling an inner twinge of guilt as she said the words—Kaspar would have missed her badly over these past weeks. Fabian looked at her in interest.

'The Oriental carpet man?'

'Yes.'

'You must be an expert, then,' he replied.

'I'm still learning.' She drew her breath. 'Do you think she'll do what you've asked? Cerise Hunniford, I mean.'

'Yes,' he nodded, 'I think she will.' The lift doors opened, and he escorted her out into the street. 'I'll let her think it over for two days, then I'll make another appointment. She won't try to get around that injunction in the meantime, so don't worry.' He glanced at his watch. 'I have to get back to the office. Will you come and see me again in six days' time?'

'Yes, of course.' She touched his sleeve. 'Will that injunction really stop her, Mr Blackthorne?'

'She could certainly challenge it,' he admitted seriously. 'Principally because you were so foolish as to sign a contract with them. It depends on how good her lawyers are—and how badly she wants to print. She'd be risking a massive fine, and possible confiscation of all copies, if she *did* try it. So I think she'll hold back for the time being. Once I get her to sign a formal agreement not to print, we'll be in business. Six days ought to see everything turn out right.' He hailed a passing taxi, then turned to her. 'Can I offer you a lift back to the City?'

'No, thanks—I'm going to pick my car up.' She didn't expect his touch on her arm.

'Cathy—can I give you some non-legal advice?'

'Of course,' she said in surprise.

'Get your life back together. Whatever's happened to it. I'll see you next week.'

She stared after him as he stepped into his taxi. He didn't wave goodbye.

Slowly she walked down the tree-lined street, thinking about his parting words. Yes, it *was* time she got her life back together again. Could it be that the nightmare was at last drawing to an end?

CHAPTER TWO

Six days later, Cathy dashed into Orientalia, Kaspar Aprahamian's carpet shop, to tell him that she was ready to come back to work.

'I can only stay a few minutes,' she said breathlessly as she ran down the stairs to meet him. The old man's face lit up.

'Catherine! Matushka!' He embraced her, his frail arms as light as birds' wings. 'But you have lost weight, child!'

'A little,' she smiled. She kissed his dry cheek gently. 'Are you all right, Kaspar?'

'Are *you* all right?' he asked in concern. 'It's over two weeks!'

'As you see me.' She pirouetted in front of him, her silk skirt swinging around hips that were admittedly more slender than they'd been a fortnight ago. She didn't want to talk about her bust-up with Tim, let alone the terrible *Caprice* episode, yet she knew she owed Kaspar some apology. 'I'm so sorry about leaving you in the lurch like that, Kaspar——'

'You don't have to apologise to Kaspar,' the Armenian said affectionately. 'Kaspar always understands.' She had been working for him for two years, drawn to the shop as much by her affection for the old man as by a lifelong love for Oriental rugs. In that time, she had grown to regard Kaspar as one of her closest friends; she had accompanied him to Turkey on two buying trips, and under his tuition her knowledge had grown to the extent that he had trusted her with several major purchases and sales. Just before the trouble with Tim had started, she'd been buying at auctions for him, as far afield as France and Germany—but as her emotional life had begun to disintegrate, she had known it would be impossible to keep working. She had decided

23

to take her summer holiday—a week that had somehow stretched to two.

He examined her face, and she knew that despite her bright, nervous smile, Kaspar's expert eyes would detect the anxiety and pain that lurked in her deep green eyes. Pity stirred his nut-brown face. 'About you and Timothy—I heard that you'd broken off the engagement. I guessed that was why you couldn't come in. I can't tell you how sorry I am.'

'These things happen,' she said lightly. One of the marvellous things about Kaspar Aprahamian was never having to explain anything. 'Yes, I needed a little time to—recuperate. My father's much better now, though— he sends you greetings. I've missed you—and this place.' She glanced around the Aladdin's cave of the oriental carpet shop, drinking in the many hundreds of beautiful Persian, Turkish and Indo-Chinese rugs that glowed on the walls and floor of the shop. Kaspar Aprahamian's was an Arabian Nights fantasy world, just off the commercial grey dignity of Bond Street, a festival of Eastern design and colour. She had loved it from the first, and had loved her work here. 'You've brought some new stock in, I see.'

'All rubbish,' he deprecated. 'Rags and patches.'

'This isn't rubbish,' she grinned, tugging at the corner of a half-buried rug. It was comparatively small, but the tight geometric pattern in red and yellow-green vibrated with life. 'Kazak,' she judged. 'Late nineteenth century. Four hundred pounds?'

'Three-seventy,' he beamed. 'You haven't lost your skills in two weeks, I see.' He turned to the ancient bronze samovar that was the centrepiece of his shop, and under which a blue flame had always burned as long as Cathy had known him. 'Tell me the truth,' he said gently, 'have you had a long enough break? Because if you want more time, you have only to ask.'

'You mean you don't want me back?' she teased.

'Want you back?' He passed her an almost-black cup of tea, and then pinched her cheek gently. 'I don't know how I've managed without you, child. I did not realise how much I depended upon you until you left.' His eyes were bright with happiness.

'I've had plenty of time,' she nodded.

'It's going to be very good to have you back. Your face makes this place lighter, like a crystal lamp.'

'Ah, sweet lies,' she smiled. 'It's good to be back here, drinking your poisonous tea.'

'Drink, drink,' he nodded. 'It's an elixir of life. In Armenia, we live to be half as old as God Himself on that tea.' He watched her drink, affection bright in his eyes. 'How beautiful you are; with that black hair and those green eyes, you are like a gypsy queen among all these gypsy colours.'

'Flatterer!' she rebuked.

'What have you been doing this past fortnight, child?'

Crying. Thinking.

Aloud, she said, 'Oh, just taking it easy. Lazing about, really.'

'Good. After such blows, one needs to rest. Before the next round with life, so to speak. And your hospital work?'

'The hospital's been closed for the past week. Most of the children go home to their parents for a week about this time. To tell you the truth,' she confessed, 'I was quite relieved. I don't think I'd have made a very good art teacher with the frame of mind I was in.'

'Still,' he smiled, 'you will have missed them.'

'I did,' Cathy admitted. 'But they're all back now. I'm going there tomorrow, to start work again. I wonder if they missed me? They have such a restricted life.' She smiled, the thought of the children making her gentle-eyed. 'Mentally handicapped children have the most amazing capacity for love, Kaspar.'

'Why, so have you, child. So have all God's innocents.'

'Innocent?' The word made her wince. 'None of us are innocent, Kaspar, least of all me.' She turned to him, her face pleading. 'Do you think that anyone in the world is truly innocent? Anyone at all?'

'Allah, someone has been hurting you,' he said under his breath. 'My poor child . . .'

Suddenly selfconscious, Cathy laughed defensively. The memory of *Caprice* was out of place in this old-world shop.

'I'm all right, honestly. I didn't mean to sound so idiotic. It was just a thought.'

'Why should you feel guilty about what happened with Tim?' he asked, shaking his head.

'It's all over now,' she said. But she wondered. Even if Fabian Blackthorne had managed to stop those pictures from publication, the memory of what she had done would always be there. True, it had faded and mellowed since the first horror, but she wondered nevertheless.

'Okay.' Kaspar probed no further. 'You'll start on Monday?'

'Yes.'

'I think it's about time you got a raise,' he mused.

'You'll do no such thing,' she smiled, setting down her cup and glancing at her watch. She was due at Fabian's office in a few minutes. 'I must fly now, Kaspar—I've got a rather important meeting. I'll see you on Monday.' She kissed him briefly. 'Wish me luck.'

'God be with you,' he called, watching her trim legs and glossy black hair as she ran back up the stairs. 'And take care!'

Walking fast, Cathy realised how much she was looking forward to going back to work. It wasn't simply a question of the good salary Kaspar paid her; she knew she had a real talent for Oriental carpets, especially antique ones. They were as much works of art as any painting or sculpture, and she loved them.

She had met Kaspar at an auction when she had been nineteen; she had been trying to buy a small Isfahan for her father's birthday, and he had been after a massive selection of Anatolian rugs; within a month she had taken the job he had offered her, and had entered the strange, wonderful world of carpet dealing.

The past week had been a strange one, spent mostly looking after her father and thinking about what had gone before. She had gone riding in the woods near her home, thinking about Fabian Blackthorne and the mess she had got herself into. Somehow, contacting Fabian had cleansed her soul, releasing her from the lonely darkness she had been in since that ghastly afternoon at the *Caprice* studio. Though nothing was yet resolved, she felt better, ready to resume her life after an interruption of nearly two weeks.

Even if Fabian Blackthorne's news was going to be bad today, at least she was no longer suicidal, at least she now felt she had the strength to face the coming ordeal. And the strength to protect her father from it.

Friday morning traffic delayed her maddeningly, but by ten past twelve the exquisite secretary (this morning in twin-set and coral) was ushering her into Fabian's consulting-room.

As before, there was something in his eyes that Cathy found deeply compelling, a power that seemed to take her breath away. As before, he was wearing a dark suit that couldn't quite tame the lithe power of his body. But he was unsmiling, his eyes expressing a cool uninterest that made her heart sink.

'I'm sorry you've had to wait so long,' he said. 'It can't have been pleasant for you. Won't you sit down?'

'Is—is everything all right?' she asked uncertainly, obeying him.

'Cerise Hunniford has signed the undertaking I drew up. She's also returned all the prints and negatives.' His tone was calm, matter-of-fact. 'In return, I've negotiated a payment of five hundred pounds to compensate Aphrodite for loss of time. Is that acceptable?'

The words were like sunshine bursting through clouds to her. She sat in stunned silence for a few seconds—and then, quite without meaning to, crumpled into tears.

'I'm sorry,' she choked. 'I always seem to be making a fool of myself in front of you. But I'm so very glad— it's as though a nightmare has ended——'

He waited for her to finish, one fist on his hip. When she looked up with a shaky smile, his tanned face was wearing a slight frown of puzzlement. 'I still don't understand what led you into doing what you did, Cathy. The whole thing seems incomprehensible to me. You——' he gestured at her clothes, the frustration in his powerful body almost visible, 'you just aren't the type.'

'What type am I?' she smiled through blurred eyes.

'You're beautiful, intelligent——' He hesitated. 'You're not the sort of person who ought to have anything to do with the seamy side of life,' he concluded, sounding awkward for the very first time since she had met him.

Cathy dried her eyes, realising quite suddenly that this man's respect was very important to her. And for some crazy, feminine reason the very preciousness of his respect made her want to challenge it.

'Are you saying that out of old-fashioned chauvinism?' she asked. 'Or just because my father happens to be Sir Cedric Milner?' His arching brows showed that he was taken aback at her reply; but she couldn't keep back the warm smile that softened what she had said. 'I'm sorry,' she apologised, 'that sounded ungracious. I just happen to have discovered that an innocent appearance can conceal a multitude of evils, Mr Blackthorne.'

'That's true,' he nodded. 'But I'm saying it because you strike me as an old-fashioned sort of woman. There's a quality about you that seems to—I don't know, repel seaminess.'

'Ah.' Again, she saw his eyes flicker at the wry smile that pulled her lips down. 'The china doll syndrome. Purity doesn't go very far in this world, Mr Blackthorne. And sometimes the seamy side of life just walks up and kicks you in the teeth.'

'Hmmm.' He opened a red-trimmed file. 'I take it you do have five hundred pounds to give Ms Hunniford?'

'I'll write you a cheque now.' There would be just about exactly that amount in her account, she realised wryly. It was about time she got back to work, and stopped sponging off Daddy.

As he watched her sign the cheque, Fabian went on, 'I'm a lawyer, not a psychoanalyst. But I'd guess there were a lot of things that led up to what you did. Am I right?'

'Yes, Mr Blackthorne,' she said drily. She passed him the cheque. 'A lot went before.' His smile was beautiful, she realised, lighting up his face and softening the rather formidable, passionate lines. Sunlight on a winter's day. And very sexy. Suddenly she was finding him very attractive indeed, and felt colour touch her cheeks. 'How did you manage to get her to drop her price?' she asked. 'Put a gun to her head?'

'Persuasion,' he replied obliquely. 'There are more ways than one of killing a cat.'

'Such as?' she probed, interested.

'Such as choking it with cream.'

'You mean you actually kept that appointment at Claridge's Hotel?' she challenged, rather unpleasantly surprised.

'I did sup with a long spoon,' he said gravely. 'I was quite safe.'

'You *like* her,' Cathy accused, aware of a totally unreasonable stab of jealousy. 'Despite all your coldness the other day, you like her, after all!'

His dark grey eyes were smoky with amusement. 'A meal with Ms Hunniford was not exactly a penance, I confess. I find her interesting.'

'And attractive?' Cathy wanted to know, fighting her urge to throw something at his handsome head.

'Perhaps,' he shrugged, '—in a hard kind of way. She certainly doesn't have your gentleness.'

'I don't think I like being compared to Cerise Hunniford,' she snapped, disturbed by the rather mixed compliment.

'I wasn't comparing you at all,' he said mildly. His eyes appraised her. 'You're utterly different. That combination of jade-green eyes and pitch-black hair is very striking.'

She stirred uncomfortably as she looked up into the storm-grey eyes. He had a very powerful, exclusively male, magnetism. But she didn't fool herself that it was directed at her personally. Had he and that dreadful woman hit it off together? Cerise had certainly been interested enough in *him*. But could he be attracted to her? She had to remind herself sharply that his private life was nothing at all to do with her.

'Mr Blackthorne,' she said quietly, 'I'm very grateful indeed for your help. You don't know what this means to me. I was so dreading the publication of those pictures. I think I'd have died with shame.' She paused, her tongue seeming to knot itself on what she wanted to say. 'As for my father—it doesn't bear thinking of. You've been so strong, so reassuring. I—I just want to say thank you.'

He stared into her eyes for a long second, then stood up, and walked with that pantherine grace to the massive safe that was set into one wall. 'There's no need for thanks,' he said. His eyes were sombre again. 'Here they are—all the prints and negatives from that studio session.'

A scarlet tide swept into Cathy's face as she stared at the envelope in his competent hands.

'In case you're wondering,' Fabian said quietly, 'I haven't opened it. I've had to take Cerise Hunniford's word that it's all in here, since I have no way of checking—though it doesn't matter, since she's legally barred from printing anything concerning you. Ever. Still, I suggest you take this home with you, and check the contents carefully. Especially the negatives. Try and remember whether all the shots you posed for are there. Understand?'

'Yes.' The word was a whisper.

'Very well.' He laid it on the desk in front of her. 'Will you let me know whether you think there's anything missing?'

'Yes,' she whispered again.

'It's best to be safe.' He waited for a reply, but Cathy's silky black head was bowed. His voice more gentle, he went on, 'Cathy, I think I know how much this has hurt you. But it's over now. And whatever went before—that's over now, too. I'm not going to lecture you. But you know where to find me if you need me.' She looked up to meet his half-smile. 'And before you mention a fee—there isn't one.'

'But——'

'Call it legal gallantry. Besides, I would hate to see any scandal to come to you or your family.'

'I'm *very* grateful.' She clutched the envelope, at a loss for words. 'Especially since you don't even know the whys and wherefores of all this——'

'I don't have to.' He stared at her consideringly. 'The Milners are old clients of this firm.'

'I'm glad I have something to recommend me,' she said, her emotions bittersweet.

'You've got considerable natural beauty,' he said unexpectedly. 'And you have a charm, and a strength of character, that makes you special. Don't let this cloud your horizon any more, whatever caused it.'

Liking him more than she had ever done, Cathy rose to her feet, still feeling a bit shaky. 'You must be a very good lawyer, Mr Blackthorne. I'll always be grateful to you—for my father's sake as well as my own.' They both hesitated, grey eyes meeting green, but there seemed nothing more to say. Fabian walked her to the oak doorway.

'What are you going to do with the pictures?' he asked.

'Burn them,' she said decisively. His handshake was firm, but there was no goodbye smile for her. Mr Blackthorne's quota of beautiful smiles, she decided, had probably been used up.

But once again, as she walked out of the elegant office, wondering whether she would ever see him again, the warmth of his touch seemed to linger on her skin and in her heart. Fabian Blackthorne must have a very strange opinion of her.

In the busy street outside she drew a deep breath of pure relief. The envelope in her arms was leaden—but it was a burden she was soon going to shed for ever.

She drove back home and parked her car on the

driveway. The garden was lovely, sweet with blossom; she walked up the path, and opened the front door on to silence. Her father was dining at his club today, she knew, and the house was deserted. Exactly the way she wanted it for what she had to do.

The big sitting room was quiet and neat. She squatted in front of the logs that always stood in the fireplace, summer and winter, and put the searing blue tongue of the gas-poker to the pile. Within minutes, a bright fire was blazing in the hearth. Nerving herself for the job, Cathy tore open the manila envelope. Inside were a spool of negative film and a sheaf of glossy photographs, some already marked for editing and cropping. She had to force herself to look at the first few. Somehow, though, they were unreal—the smooth skin of her own body, the lustrous sweep of her raven hair, these could have belonged to anyone. Her own oval face looked back at her, as cool as though there hadn't been a fire raging in her brain that day, hotter and more savage than the one she was now sitting in front of.

Revenge. That was what had driven her to the studio that night. The blind, almost mad need to hurt Tim the way he had hurt her . . .

Cathy stared at the glossy paper, oddly aware of a slight inner sense of relief. The pictures weren't as sordid and as horrible as she'd feared in her darkest moments. The photographer's mist had artfully concealed much. Some, though, were direct enough to whip the colour into her cheeks. It was a shock, after all, to see her own body so sexually and shamelessly presented. She tossed the photographs abruptly on to the fire, disturbed. The crackling flames licked upwards, consuming and cleansing.

She stared into the flames with unseeing eyes, each green pupil containing a reflected glow. It was all unreeling in her mind, like a bad old movie, a sordid, ill-made, confused movie, in which the reels had become mixed. She was remembering Tim's face, remembering her own stupid happiness, the months that had slowly turned to nightmare. She could taste her own pain and frustration again, feel that old ache at her apparent inability to get Tim to respond to her love for him. Her terror at the thought that she might be sexually unattractive to him. Her dread that the reason they could never make love lay in her own frigidity. Then the last desperate days, as she had tried to salvage what was left of their engagement. And then the ultimate revelation of Tim's inner character.

God! It had taken her so long to discover what he was *really* like, why their relationship had *really* never worked.

And when she had made that discovery, she had run crying into the street, feeling as though she wanted to die. She had used alcohol, for the first time in her life, to try and quench that pain, while her mind searched for some action she could take, something she could do that would strike back at the man she had thought she loved, and punish him the way he had punished her. And the brilliant lights of the studio, the alcohol in her blood never quite numbing her to the madness of what she was doing . . .

Slowly the movie flickered and died, fading away to ashes with the twisting photographs in the heart of the flames. Working carefully, she laid each strip of negatives on to the flame, watching them flash and writhe into nothingness. When the last of the photographs was gone, she burned the envelope, too, and used a poker to crush any fragments that might remain.

When she was quite sure that it was all utterly gone, she curled up on the sofa, hugging her knees, and gazed dreamily into the fire, now burning bright and clean.

Gone. The nightmare was just a memory now. And it was as though her fire had consumed the last of her anger against Tim into the same ashes. There was still an ache for him there. There probably would be for a long time to come. But she knew, as she gazed absently into the flame, that she could no longer blame him. Now that she had accepted the inevitability of the fact that they could never have made it together, she was seeing things a lot clearer.

It was time for forgiveness. And pity.

The Addington Hospital, where Cathy worked part-time, was a rambling, red-brick Victorian mansion set in six acres of pleasant woodland, five miles or less from Cathy's home in Northwood. Most of the children here went home to their parents for a week in the summer, and the place had just opened up again after its short break. As she walked through the main reception area, she realised how much she had missed the children.

The first people she met were Ursula, possibly her favourite pupil of all, and Jean Robson, one of the senior staff nurses. Ursula broke free from Jean's hand with a little cry, and galloped on ungainly legs to meet Cathy. Her little Mongol face, usually expressionless, was alight with pleasure.

'Everyone went home to their mummies,' Ursula accused. 'Except me. Why didn't you come and see me?'

'I didn't know you were still here,' smiled Cathy, squatting to take Ursula's uncontrolled hands in her own. 'But I'm back now. Are you all right, Ursie?'

'She's got a bit of a cold,' Jean Robson volunteered, walking up with a smile. She withdrew one hand from the capacious pockets of her uniform to give Cathy a warm handshake. 'It's good to see you again.'

'Did you have a good holiday?' asked Cathy.

'Very good, thanks.'

'I want to start painting now,' Ursula was commanding, her almond eyes turning from one adult to the other pleadingly. 'Can't we paint now?'

'Tomorrow afternoon,' Cathy promised. 'If Dr Holland will let you.' The little hand, clinging to her own so trustingly, reawakened poignant memories of her work here, and she turned to Jean Robson. 'Jean, I'm going up to see Dr Holland in a minute. Could I drop into the ward first? Just to say hullo to the children?'

'Of course,' the nurse agreed, leading the way. As Ursula trotted unsteadily beside Cathy—her legs were more or less uncontrolled at times—she was chattering about the paintings she was going to do tomorrow. 'Apparently she was rather miserable here,' Jean confided. 'Well, she would be. Most of the kids went home.'

'I didn't realise that she was going to be staying,' said Cathy. As a volunteer worker here, she wasn't supposed to know anything about the children's families, and she had to tread carefully in that respect.

'She does have a mother,' Jean said quietly. 'But the mother almost never comes to see Ursie. It's a shame, really. Come right through.'

The J. L. Taylor Ward contained twenty-three children in two sections. The first, which contained most of Cathy's pupils, was reserved for the more co-ordinated patients, and it was here that she now greeted an impromptu welcoming committee, intent on receiving her with noisy delight.

The Mongols, she noticed, were as always the most affectionate, clinging to her hands and laughing; but the disturbed children were responding, too, the clouds lifting from their eyes as they gathered around her.

'When can we start painting?' Robin was demanding eagerly. Brutal treatment in his infancy had left him with limbs that were barely controllable and a mind that shied away from all concentration—but between his rambling fingers a paintbrush had acquired an almost magical power, and he had been one of her most promising pupils.

'Soon,' she promised, 'as soon as we can. Hullo, Tugger.'

'Hullo, Cathy!' Tugger bawled joyfully, like a big puppy who had only been waiting attention to explode with happiness. His eighteen-year-old body contained the mind of an amiable four-year-old; Tugger was technically due for transfer to an adult ward, but he was so obviously at home among the other children that the doctors had decided to leave him there for the time being. 'I got some new shells for my collection!'

'I can't wait to see them.' Among the babble and laughter around her, she noticed that John-Paul was, as ever, standing back by the window, a haunted figure whose shadowy eyes pleaded for help. She disentangled herself from eager hands to make her way over to him. He looked up at her from under his fringe with squinting blue eyes. 'Hullo, John-Paul,' she said gently. 'Remember me?' He just stared at her, unmoving. 'Cathy,' she said in the same quiet voice. 'Remember Cathy?' She thought she could see shadows of understanding moving under the pale features. 'You used to love my painting classes—remember?'

'Painting,' he repeated. He was the most difficult and inaccessible of all the little personalities at the Addington. But just as she was about to turn away, he reached for her hand and led her to his bunk. Silent, she waited as he knelt by his bedside cabinet, scrabbling inside. He withdrew something, and handed it to her.

'Car,' he said. It was a crumpled painting he had done in one of her classes, a series of red splotches that dimly formed the shape of her car.

'Yes,' she nodded with a smile. 'My car. We're going to start painting again soon. Remember how you used to enjoy that?' Two of the Mongol children were bouncing on the bed now, demanding attention, but she persevered, determined to make John-Paul respond again. 'Remember the cows you painted? Would you like to start painting again?'

The pale face twisted as he crouched on the floor, hugging his knees.

'Yes,' he said suddenly. 'I want to paint again.'

'Good boy,' she said happily, leaning forward to hug him. Ursula and Tricia were clambering on to her shoulders now, their surprisingly strong arms twining around her as they clamoured for her attention. Laughing, she found herself at the centre of a minor scrimmage of children.

'Working your magic as usual?' She looked up into Oliver Holland's brown eyes. Under his trim black beard he was smiling gently. 'How is it you always manage to turn this ward into a fairground, Cathy?'

'Hullo, Oliver.' She rose to shake his hand, Ursula gathered under left arm. 'How was your break?'

'Not as good as seeing you.' He held her hand tightly, his expression warm. 'Are you coming back to teach tomorrow?'

'If it's convenient.'

The young doctor released her hand at last.

'Of course it's convenient. I don't know what we'd all do without you, Cathy.'

'I've missed them all,' Cathy nodded, preferring to ignore the meaning in the doctor's eyes. The last thing she wanted right now was to face Oliver Holland's determined adoration of her. But he was obviously not going to be put off.

'Let's talk in my office,' he said, taking her arm. 'Will you take charge, please, Jean?'

'Of course.' The nurse shot a knowing look at Cathy as Oliver walked her out of the ward. His crush on Cathy Milner was obvious to the entire staff at the Addington, and had been presenting her with something of a problem almost from the beginning.

'You look tired, Cathy,' he said as she sat down in his office. His eyes searched her. 'And you've lost a lot of weight. Have you been sick?'

'Not exactly,' said Cathy, not wanting to elaborate.

'Then what, exactly?'

'I was just a bit run down,' she hedged. She had never liked Oliver's propensity for direct questions, a habit common with many doctors. He lowered his slim frame into the chair opposite, his thin face—with the Van Dyck beard, it always reminded her of a seventeenth century portrait—expressing thoughtful concern.

'I heard that you and Tim Coryat broke off the engagement,' he probed. 'Was that why you've been— "run down"?' She didn't deny it, but her expression apparently warned Oliver not to pursue the topic right now. 'The kids always love this holiday,' he said, changing the subject. 'No hospital can replace family care. It's a pity that more parents can't cope.'

'This hospital gives them a family,' Cathy smiled.

'And you make a very special contribution to that family feeling, Cathy.' His eyes were intent. 'The response you get out of them is something remarkable. I'd never have believed it if I hadn't seen it with my own eyes—children who didn't respond to any known medical treatment suddenly taking an interest in something. Suddenly having something to live for. No medication or psychotherapy could do that.'

'I think it's the therapy of painting rather than just me,' she smiled. 'Painting is one of the most direct forms of self-expression you can get—and you don't have to be articulate or literate or clever to do it.'

'It's more than that,' the doctor said earnestly. 'There's something about you, Cathy—something that makes even the most difficult children respond immediately. You're really very talented with them. And there's a warmth about you that——' He hesitated, and Cathy's heart sank. Oliver was inevitably coming round to a topic she dreaded.

'I spoke to John-Paul, the autistic boy,' she said brightly. 'He remembered me perfectly.'

'Cathy,' Oliver said seriously, ignoring that remark, 'now that you and Tim have broken up, maybe you'll have a little more time for other people. Well, I think you know how I feel about you. I know it's a little soon, but maybe we could see each other a bit more now.'

'Oliver, I'm very flattered, but——'

'I really think that given a chance, you and I could get to know each other a lot better,' he pressed on. 'Seeing you brightens up this whole place. I've missed you, too. There were plenty of times I wanted to phone during this past week, but I held myself back. Maybe now's the time to start . . .'

For a doctor, Oliver was remarkably insensitive, Cathy sighed inwardly as he talked earnestly on. For all his formal manner, there was something juvenile about him. She compared him mentally to Fabian asking her out, she knew she would probably have accepted. But Oliver Holland——

'Oliver,' she said quietly, cutting through his plans for a weekend in Scotland, 'please listen. I come here to work—because I love the children, and because I think in my small way I can do something for them. I like all the staff. I like Jean Robson, and Dr Lorenz. And I like you.' His face fell, the dark beard giving him a melancholy look. 'Breaking up with Timothy wasn't easy—and I'm still not ready for anything else, not even the admittedly pleasant things you're talking about.'

'I don't want an emotional commitment,' Oliver put in, 'just the opportunity to see you a bit more. Outside of a work context, that is.'

'My work with Kaspar Aprahamian is very demanding.' She tried to keep her smile friendly, but final. 'You know that I work full-time, five days a week, and some weekends as well. On top of that, I come here three times a week to give the children their painting lesson, and that can extend well into the evening. Besides that, you know my father had a bad heart attack at the beginning of the year. He's still not well—and there's only a housekeeper at home to look after him. I'm the one who really cares for him, keeps him company, cooks his meals.' She took a breath. 'Outside of a work context, Oliver, I sleep.'

'But, Cathy——'

'And that's the way I want it,' she said firmly. 'For the time being, at least. I'm sorry to sound fierce, but I'm really not prepared for any more emotional responsibilities yet.'

For a minute she thought he was going to argue further, and registered real dismay; but even Oliver Holland couldn't miss the determination in her face.

'Okay,' he shrugged, still not conceding defeat. 'We'll talk about it some other time. I don't think you understand how serious I am about you, Cathy.' He stared at her soft, full lips and her short, straight nose, then up to the wide eyes that were such an intriguing shade of jade green, fringed with thick black lashes. For the thousandth time he thought that she was one of the loveliest women he had ever seen. And, on occasion, one of the most determined. He took one of her hands in both his own, his thin lips tight with emotion. 'I'm very serious.'

Gently, she withdrew her hands and stood up, dreading another argument. 'I must get back to my father now - -he frets when I'm away too long. It was nice seeing you, Oliver, and seeing all the children. I'll be along on Tuesday afternoon, around four-thirty. Can you get us that playroom again?'

'No problem,' he promised, following her to the door, and down the unhospital-like corridors to the door. 'And if you have any problems, you know my number.'

'Of course.' She slipped quickly into her Metro, ducking what looked like an approaching goodbye kiss, waved brightly, and drove off down the gravelled driveway.

If Oliver was going to persist in his pursuit of her, she realised with dismay, her pleasure in her work at the Addington was going to be destroyed. He had been pressing even while she had been engaged to Timothy Coryat, and though she had tried to tell herself it was merely bonhomie, she now realised that he was seriously interested in her.

A bitter twist crossed her mouth as she drove along leafy lanes towards Northwood. Maybe he wouldn't be so keen if he knew that her naked body had almost adorned the centre pages of a near-pornographic magazine.

Fabian Blackthorne must have worked hard to get those pictures back, she thought obliquely. A flood of gratitude to him filled her heart as she looked up through her windscreen at a sky that was bluer and warmer than it had been for months. She could trust a man like Fabian. Men like Tim (and Oliver Holland, to be frank) had a weakness about them that could either be meltingly soft—or treacherously marshy.

The memory of Fabian's grey, compelling eyes stayed in her mind, a presence that was warm and vaguely exciting. He was a very *masculine* man, that was certain. Assured, confident, and yet not pompous. Whereas Oliver . . .

Anyway, what was she doing, thinking about men? She cornered carefully, and nosed the car up the rather overgrown driveway that led up to the manor house where she and her father continued to live, even though it was now much too large after her mother's departure. When Mummy had been here, she reflected, walking inside, there had always been a flock of servants in attendance, streams of visitors and admirers.

Coincidentally, it was about her mother that she and her father began to talk over dinner that night. She had long ago realised that her father, a prominent Liberal M.P. knighted for services in Parliament and in the last world war, was not a man given to much sentiment. That, maybe, partly accounted for the break-up of his marriage four years ago, when her mother had suddenly announced that she was leaving for France with another man, to the horror of a seventeen-year-old Cathy.

Since his heart attack, though, he had been much more affectionate towards his only daughter, and more demonstrative in general, as though he sensed that his remaining time might be short.

'I've had another letter from that Frenchman, asking for money,' he said over the roast lamb, and Cathy pulled a face. Her mother's intentions of marrying her Frenchman had soon evaporated, and she was now in Spain with what Cathy assumed must be her third lover in succession. The first had now taken to pestering Sir Cedric for money, an addition of insult to injury which he bore with amazing patience.

'I don't know why you don't just explode,' she sighed.

'I'm coming to the end of my patience, I confess.' His wrinkled kindly face smiled up at her. 'I'm going to hand the whole thing over to young Blackthorne. He'll know what to do.'

'Fabian Blackthorne?'

'Yes. The old man's retired now, you know. But his son's a damned good lawyer. Nice chap.'

'Yes,' said Cathy, helping him to more mint sauce, 'I know.'

Her father looked up mildly. 'I didn't know you'd met him?'

'I——' She flushed slightly. 'Only socially.'

'As a matter of fact, your Aunt Leila wrote to me the other day.' He dabbed his lips and sighed. 'Says your mother's got herself another man—a Portuguese count, I believe.'

'Oh lord,' Cathy winced. 'He must be the fourth!'

'Something like that.' Cedric Milner had Cathy's green eyes, and they now looked at his daughter with something like embarrassment. 'It's not very nice for you,' Cathy. I know that parents are meant to set their children a good example, give them something to look up to. Your mother and I don't seem to have done very well.'

'That wasn't your fault, Daddy.' She patted his hand, thinking how frail and old he had become over the past months. 'You've been a wonderful father to me. And as for Mummy—well, she was wonderful too. At the time that it mattered from my point of view, anyway. Her running off like that——' She hesitated. 'Some women have a much harder change of life than others, you know. Maybe she'll get over this stage and come back some day.'

'I keep forgetting how perceptive you are,' he smiled quietly. 'It wasn't so long ago that you weren't supposed to know about things like the change of life.'

'I'm twenty-one,' she protested.

'Ancient,' he agreed solemnly, his bony, aristocratic face teasing her.

'Would you take her?' She glanced up at him. 'If she wanted to come back? You're not divorced, after all— only separated.'

For a minute she thought she might have said the wrong thing, but then her father sighed.

'Take Genevieve back? I felt very bitter when she left, Cathy. I wouldn't have wanted to see her again, I don't think—if it weren't for the coronary.' He touched his heart, his eyes thoughtful. 'Since this happened, I've seen the world through new eyes, seen the importance of forgiveness, of understanding—and seen how badly we all need love and compassion. Yes, I'd take her back. We shared a lot, you know. For most of our marriage she was a good and loyal wife. As you've been a good and loyal daughter.' He patted her cheek, his palm warm. 'More than good—an angel.'

'Flattery will get you everywhere,' she chuckled.

'Will it get me a cigar?'

'You know the doctor said——'

'Ach!' Sir Cedric stood up, wincing slightly with the effort, and putting an arm around his daughter, walked with her to the drawing-room. 'What the hell do doctors know? Let's have a cigar *and* a glass of port.'

'I'll skip the cigar,' she mused, 'but I'll join you in the port.'

'Celebrating?' He winced again as he lowered himself into his favourite armchair.

'Yes,' she nodded, a faint smile tugging at her lips. 'Yes, I do have something to celebrate.'

'I thought you were looking better than you'd done in weeks,' he said. 'I was worried about you, and I don't mind saying so. You looked terrible these past few days.'

'I'm better now,' she said, and he noticed without commenting that this time the smile reached her eyes. 'I'm much better now.'

CHAPTER THREE

LIKE most of Mala Elphinstone's ideas, Cathy thought to herself, the party was turning out a success. Mala herself, a tall and portly woman in a buttercup-yellow kaftan that ought to have looked garish but didn't, was holding court in the centre of the room. She had deliberately invited people from as many walks of life she could think of—beside Cathy, a trade union leader was discussing the merits of a second-hand Rolls-Royce with a well-known Member of Parliament—and the sometimes outrageous mixtures gave the whole get-together a likely sparkle.

Cathy had hesitated before coming, wondering whether she could cope; but had decided that she couldn't spend the rest of her life in hiding. Now she was glad she had come. She glanced round the crowded, happy room again before turning her attention politely back to the man from the Finnish trade delegation, who was extolling the merits of Finnish caviare in a heavy accent.

'Do you know Mala well?' she asked, trying to steer him away from the salty topic of caviare—it was graded, he was telling her enthusiastically, like shotgun pellets.

'Of course. Mala and I are old friends.' He gave the hostess a cheery wave across the room, and returned hungrily to the habits of the Arctic sturgeon. Cathy groaned inwardly, eyeing the more interesting-looking groups surreptitiously. It was always her luck to end up with the party bore, prevented by inborn compassion from escaping.

And then, across the room, she caught a glimpse of a tall masculine figure moving through the crowd. Her heart jolted with a force that almost made her gasp. Without thinking, she threw a quick excuse to the man

44

from the Finnish trade delegation, and hustled her way urgently towards the tall man, spilling her drink on the way.

It *was* Fabian! Feeling her heart beating quite foolishly, she made her way up to him, and greeted him with a nervous little, 'Hullo, Mr Blackthorne.'

He turned to her in surprise, those forceful eyes searching hers for a split second, and then the heart-warming smile she remembered so well crossed his mouth.

'Hullo, Cathy.' He was holding a drink in each hand, his dark grey suit suggesting that he had come to the party straight from work. 'Please don't be so formal, though. My name's Fabian. You don't mind my calling you Cathy?'

'Of course not,' she said hastily. He made her feel impossibly nervous, perhaps because of her embarrassment at what he knew about her. But as she looked up at him, she realised with numb surprise that he was really one of the most handsome men she had ever met. Why hadn't she noticed that before? And there was a hint of brooding passion about the deep grey eyes and the rather full mouth that conveyed a darkly aggressive sexual appeal. 'I've just been talking to a man from the Finnish trade delegation,' she stammered, trying to find a sensible topic of conversation. 'Did you know that caviare is graded, like shot?'

'I did,' he said gravely. There was amusement in the storm-grey eyes. 'Is your father well?'

'He's doing fine,' she said grasping gratefully at something to talk about. 'Have you managed to put that Frenchman off?'

'The one who kept asking for money? I wrote him a stiff letter which ought to make him think twice, anyway. I didn't realise that he and your mother hadn't married in the end.' Catching sight of her involuntary grimace, he went on, 'I'm sorry. It's a sensitive topic, I can see that.'

'I get used to it,' she smiled wryly. He was at least a foot taller than she, and she had to look up into his face, feeling acutely conscious of his splendid build. 'She's in Spain now, with her latest—er—her latest friend. One day she'll settle down, I guess.'

'You haven't seen her since she and your father parted?'

'No. And she doesn't write much, either.' Cathy shrugged, covering up pain. 'We're a peculiar sort of family, I suppose.' She stared down into her empty glass, wondering what to say next.

'Here.' Gently he took it from her fingers, and gave her one of the full glasses he was carrying. 'You look very attractive tonight, anyway. I like that dress.' His eyes were on the silky slopes of her naked shoulders. The off-the-shoulder floral dress had actually come from a Harrods sale, but it looked at least a hundred pounds more elegant. The simple lines emphasised the clear-cut beauty of her neck and throat, and her skin was fine enough to show off. 'I have to say that you look a lot happier than when we first met.'

'Was I very down-looking?' she laughed.

'You're a different woman,' he smiled, his eyes flattering her smokily.

'I probably am,' she nodded earnestly, delighted by his praise, even if it was only polite small-talk. 'You took a lot of worry off my mind.'

'All in a day's work,' he said lightly. 'Are you with anyone tonight?' Cathy shook her head, her heart beating faster. For a moment she was sure he was going to ask her to join him, but he seemed to change his mind abruptly. 'A beautiful woman like you shouldn't be unescorted,' he smiled. 'Which reminds me— someone at the office was telling me that you were engaged to Timothy Coryat for a while? I take it that's no longer on?'

'No,' she said with an effort. It had been rather a shock hearing Tim's name on his lips. 'Did you—did you know Tim?'

'We played tennis a few times. My firm did some legal business for the stockbrokers he worked for.' He drank, obviously hesitating before opening what was apparently another sensitive topic for her. Cathy smiled suddenly.

'There aren't too many topics in my life suitable for small-talk, are there? Timothy Coryat and I broke up last month. The week that I came to see you, in fact. We haven't seen each other since.'

The dark grey eyes searched hers intently. 'Any regrets?'

'That's not a very fair question,' she retorted. Deliberately she moved her body away from his, as though he were a fire that was too warm for comfort. She was becoming increasingly aware of his effect on her. The commanding, almost dominating quality of his presence was like an underwater current that tugged at her senses, sending ripples right through her being. Trying not to reveal how disconcerting she found him, she smiled as calmly as she could. 'All break-ups are traumatic. There were simply too many differences between Tim and me for us to carry on.'

'I see.'

'Did you—like him?'

'He was all right.' Fabian shrugged. 'To be quite frank, I didn't pay him all that much attention. Which I would have done,' he added with a glint, 'if I'd known what a stunningly attractive fiancée he had. But if you'll forgive me, there didn't seem to me to be too much to him.'

No, Cathy thought; to someone as virile and bright as Fabian Blackthorne, Tim would seem an insubstantial, almost shadowy person. What had there been about him to inspire so much feeling in her? When you came down to looking at it, nothing. Just the fact that he was *there*, a rock to cling on to when her mother and father were breaking apart. A rock that had proved disastrously unstable . . .

'Hey!' She blinked as his palm brushed her cheek gently. 'You've gone into a trance!'

'Oh—sorry.' Flushing at the sensuous touch of his fingers against her skin, she met his amused eyes in some confusion. 'I was just thinking. It's a nice party, isn't it?'

'Fun,' he nodded. 'Which reminds me that I was on my way to rejoin my partner. Unfortunately, you've hijacked her drink.' She smiled as he made his way back to the drinks table to get another glass of wine, but inwardly was repeating, *her* drink? Who was he with? 'It was nice talking to you,' he said, returning with full glasses. Cathy kept her smile firmly in place, though she was fully aware of the dismissal in his voice. And of the lack of an invitation to join him and his partner.

'Who used to win?' she asked as a sudden afterthought.

'What?'

'When you and Timothy played tennis. Who used to win?'

'Oh. I did.' Fabian's dark brows came down in thought. 'I don't think he was very good.'

'No,' she nodded, 'I don't suppose he was.'

'Do you play?' he asked, poised to leave.

'Well—I used to play a bit of squash,' she replied.

'We must have a game some time,' he smiled. And although his mind was clearly on other things, and the invitation a polite social nothing, her heart jumped.

'That would be lovely,' she said eagerly.

'Good,' he nodded, but didn't bother about fixing a time or place. 'I'll probably see you around, then——'

'Ah,' said a smooth female voice, 'so *this* is where you've been!'

Cathy turned to face the newcomer. Cerise Hunniford's bright blue eyes met hers with an almost vicious glint. She was startlingly attractive tonight, her flame-red hair set off by a clinging green dress. She slid one scarlet-nailed hand firmly through the crook of Fabian's arm.

It was as though iced water had been dashed into Cathy's face. *Cerise?* With Fabian Blackthorne?

'Good evening, Miss Hunniford,' she heard her own voice saying.

'I see you're enjoying the party,' said Cerise, still smiling.

'It's been very pleasant,' Cathy nodded, not adding the bitchy *up till now* that was on the tip of her tongue.

'Indeed.' Her eyes raked Cathy from head to foot. 'I didn't really look at you the last time we met. Your pictures don't do you justice, Miss Milner. Do they, darling?' She fluttered her lashes innocently at Fabian. 'I've been getting thirstier and thirstier back there. I wondered where you'd got to. But now I see you had good reason to be detained.' Cerise's fake-posh accent, Cathy realised, was a careless veneer spikily underlaid with East End cockney—Cerise's way, she guessed, of giving the world a V-sign.

Cerise snuggled closer to Fabian, clearly wanting to signal her possession. A crackle of anger shot through Cathy's veins. She'd been right after all, it seemed. Fabian's interest in Cerise Hunniford was no joke. Her eyes flicked to Fabian's face, and caught his faint smile.

'Cathy,' he purred in his deep voice, 'you're giving me what used to be known as an old-fashioned look. Can I ask why?'

'Maybe I'm an old-fashioned girl,' she retorted, her eyes searching his face briefly. She had never respected anyone the way she had respected Fabian, and her sense of betrayal was sharp and clear, even though she knew it was unreasonable. Why shouldn't he go out with whom he pleased? 'I had no idea that the legal profession was so convivial,' she couldn't help saying bitterly. 'It must give your clients great confidence to see you on intimate terms with their opponents.'

'Cathy,' Fabian said quietly, 'for one thing, I don't make a habit of getting intimate with either my clients or their opponents. We simply happen to have been out a few times, that's all. For another, you and Cerise were never exactly opponents, anyway, or I wouldn't be here with her. And finally, anything between us has nothing to do with your case.'

'Oh, don't explain,' Cathy retorted, biting back her temper. 'I realise that I'm woefully ignorant of the niceties of legal protocol.' It was just beginning to dawn on her that Fabian might have obtained Cerise's agreement about those pictures by far less innocent means than a dinner at Claridges. And it was horrible to feel that Fabian and this woman might be lovers, united against her, that she was somehow naked to them.

'Then let's not quarrel,' Fabian smiled. 'Cathy has been telling me about caviare,' he went on. 'Apparently it's graded, like shot.'

'Or like tarts,' Cerise Hunniford said succinctly. The word dropped like a stone into the conversation. Obviously enjoying the icy whiteness in Cathy's cheeks, she went on, 'There are big tarts, and there are little tarts. Speaking personally, I feel that if you're going to go in for something, you might as well go in for it in a big way. But there will always be a place, no doubt,' she smiled brightly, 'for the little tart.'

'I think that's enough, Cerise,' Fabian growled.

'Please don't defend me, Mr Blackthorne,' said Cathy in a still, cold voice. 'I don't need it.'

'Why, you've gone quite pale, child,' cooed Cerise, feigning surprise.

'It must be the proximity of such colourful people,' she said, forcing a dry smile to her lips. 'I don't want to come between you any more, so if you'll excuse me——'

'Cathy.' Fabian's touch on her arm stopped her. His eyes were serious. 'Don't go.'

'I'm sure Miss Milner has things to do,' said Cerise, not at all pleased by Fabian's intervention. 'She wants to leave.'

'But I don't want her to leave just yet. And I think you should apologise, Cerise.'

'Why, *Fabian*!' There was malice in Cerise's smile. 'You're an absolute Sir Galahad!'

'Why should Miss Hunniford apologise?' Cathy asked icily. 'I want nothing from her, let alone an insincere apology.'

'Please,' Fabian said quietly, 'I wish you two would try and come to terms with each other. There was a misunderstanding between you, but that's long since been cleared up.'

'I always said you had a sentimental spot for little

Miss Milner,' purred Cerise. '*I* know what it is! You had a peek at those photographs, after all, didn't you?'

'You're being nasty,' Fabian said calmly, though his eyes were angry. 'I didn't see the pictures in question.'

'Oh, come now,' Cerise smiled, hugging his arm closer against the swell of her breast, 'I told you I was nasty when first we went out, didn't I? And don't tell me you could resist taking just a *little* peek?'

'Cerise,' he said quietly, 'drop it.'

'As you wish, darling.' She laid her flame-red head against his broad shoulder, and stared brightly at Cathy. 'I'd love to come to terms with Miss Milner. In fact,' she simpered, 'I have to thank you for involuntarily introducing me to the sexiest man in the world. You don't know how grateful I am——'

'We'd best go and dance, Cerise,' said Fabian in a quiet voice, as though sensing that the situation could only get worse. 'I'm sorry this has happened, Cathy. Give my regards to your father.'

'I will,' she nodded flatly, not responding to the warmth in his eyes. Cerise gave Cathy a triumphant smile and an exaggerated bow.

Cathy's fists were clenched with anger as she watched them turn away. For the very first time in her life, she had come close to lashing out at another human being—Cerise Hunniford. And Cerise had been right, horribly so. The antagonism between them had had very little to do with the *Caprice* episode—and a lot to do with Fabian Blackthorne.

She turned away, and made her way blindly through the crowd. Cerise's mocking laughter floated after her.

At the door, Mala Elphinstone reached out a hand to stop her.

'Cathy? What's the matter, darling?'

'Nothing,' she muttered through clenched teeth. 'I'm sorry, Mala—I must get home.'

'You're crying! Has someone been wretched to you?' Her brown eyes raked the room threateningly. 'Who's been upsetting you?'

'No one.' She shook away the tears that betrayed her

eyes, trying to get a grip on her trembling fury. 'Just my own stupid self, as usual.'

'Well, don't rush off—come and have a quiet drinkie with Mala,' the tall woman in yellow insisted. 'We'll go up to my bedroom and have a nice, quiet chat——'

'Some other time, please, Mala. I'm grateful, but——'

'You haven't been looking well for weeks, Cathy. And I hear that you and Timothy Coryat have broken off your engagement. What is it? What's going wrong? You've got to talk to someone——'

'Not now.' With a pale smile, Cathy leaned forward to kiss Mala's plump cheek. 'You're so kind, Mala. But right now, I think I want to be alone.'

'Like Greta Garbo.' Mala's heavy eyelids dropped with weary compassion. 'All right, petal. But if ever you want someone to talk to, any help at all—*anything*— you know where to find me.'

'Thanks,' Cathy nodded numbly, squeezing Mala's hand, and pushed through the door into the summer night outside.

Dear God, what a fool she'd been! She let herself into her car, and accelerated heedlessly down the driveway.

Nausea rose in her soul. Fabian, with that woman! And she had been on the brink of imagining that he might be interested in her! Her anger was turning against him now. She could understand Cerise wanting to defend her interest in a man like Fabian, but what on earth could Fabian see in a woman like that, a woman who dealt in soft porn for a living? Only raw sexual attraction could possibly draw them together. And Cerise was probably highly attractive sexually, with that streak of malice. There had been a cruelty, an *enjoyment* about the little scene back there that had bitten into Cathy's heart. A message as direct as any taunt—you want him, and I've got him.

Yes, she *did* want Fabian. Cerise had seen that in her, more sharply than she had seen it herself. From the first time she had met him, she had been pulled towards him like iron to a magnet. Inexplicable, illogical and primitive. But the force was there, deep inside her, making her yearn towards him even now. A force so strong that driving away from him was a kind of tearing.

She stamped her foot down on the accelerator, as though by speed alone she could blot out her pain, her confusion.

By some chance irony, Cathy caught a glimpse of Timothy Coryat on her way home from work a few days later.

It had been a demanding day—besides the normal work of the shop, she had had to rush between two auction sales at opposite ends of London to bid for a selection of rugs that Kaspar wanted. There had been plenty of competition, and she had been forced into paying a higher price than she had intended. And in the afternoon she had had the tiring physical work of shifting the rugs into the van they used, and driving them back to Orientalia.

Driving home in the evening, Tim's figure had suddenly appeared in front of her at a traffic light, hurrying across the pedestrian crossing with bowed head.

Cathy braced herself for the emotional shock that seeing him would bring—but there had been almost nothing. She watched the slight figure in the tweed jacket she knew so well, and thought only, *how small he looks*. The lights changed, and she drove on.

A curious, empty encounter. At least, though, her lack of reaction showed how distanced she had already become from Tim and the final disastrous flare-up between them. Oh, she had learned to forgive him now. In a crazy way, doing something as crazy as going to *Caprice* had burned Tim out of her heart. But you couldn't expect a relationship of nearly three years' standing to just pass away as though it had never been.

Or could you? There was so little to Tim, with his sandy hair and sandy eyes and sand-freckled skin. When she had been eighteen. Tim's age and stability—

he was a successful stockbroker in his late twenties even then—had been very attractive to her. But over the period of their relationship, a crucial period in any woman's life, Cathy had—well, *outgrown* him. She winced as she thought the word; it sounded so callous. But wasn't that the truth?

For all his apparent maturity, Tim had been immature in some deep way that Cathy was not. Maybe it was his very immaturity that had led him into avenues of sexual experience which would repel most people. She had known that he had had a lover for some time before the end. What she hadn't known, though, had shocked her profoundly.

Tim needed to be punished. He took his pleasure from being humiliated and beaten—sado-masochism, wasn't that what they called it? It had taken her three years to find that out, and when she had finally done so, she had reacted with all the unbearable hurt of a child. What Tim needed was help. Or someone who would enjoy giving him the stimulation he needed.

Anyway, she thought wearily, it was all over now. Yet in comparison to Fabian Blackthorne, Tim was simply a nonentity, a shadowy boy. Fabian's maturity was real, not assumed. His compelling presence was unlike anything Cathy had ever felt. He was exciting, even formidable. Maybe not an easy man to know—she had the instinctive impression that Fabian was a complex and passionate personality—but an easy man to love.

And Timothy Coryat had never been lovable. He had been respectful, almost fawning, towards her father; and yet Sir Cedric had never liked him. Cathy knew that instinctively, and had grieved for it, though her father would never have dreamed of saying anything, and had always made Tim welcome. He simply hadn't inspired confidence. There was a weakness in his pale eyes, a petulance around his mouth and chin, which in her most dispassionate moments Cathy had been forced to notice.

There would always be a place in her memory for Tim.

He had been the first man ever to take a serious interest in her. And it had been in his arms that she had first learned the fumbling, trembling steps of physical desire. Again, Cathy winced. How complicated sex had been between them! Looking back, she now had a better idea why. The final revelation had shed much light on Tim's character, light that had been missing for three years. But even when he managed with his inexpert kisses to awaken her passion, she had always resisted. It was with deep relief now that she could look back and realise that she had never slept with Tim. At the time, her refusal to do so had been a most bitter subject between them. Somehow, she couldn't respond to him.

The fact that he found her extremely desirable had only made things worse.

Perhaps it had been a physical revulsion to his body itself, not that he was ugly or ill-made. Certainly, she had never considered herself a very moral person, and her refusal to let Tim make love to her hadn't been a deep conviction. She simply didn't desire him. She simply liked him better with his clothes on, when they were doing something that interested them both. And she had had to admit, in the end, that that wasn't a very good basis for a romantic relationship.

She parked on the gravel outside the ivy-covered front of the house, and went inside to find her father. As usual at this time of the evening, he was in the garden, taking advantage of the late sunlight to spray his beloved roses.

It's not that I'm frigid, she thought, standing on the patio and watching him. Some women simply don't like sex. But I'm not one of them—I know it. I know it, deep inside.

It wasn't true to say she had never responded to Timothy Coryat. She had. She had felt the desire running in her veins like fire, felt the excitement that quickened her heart and made her breathing come fast and ragged.

Yet it had been so impersonal, somehow. As though her body was responding, but not her mind . . .

She bit her lip hard. Ironic that she should have been the means of bringing Cerise and Fabian together. Were they already lovers? Probably. Cerise didn't look the platonic type. And Fabian, with that brooding passion in his mouth and eyes, would be a man who would be physically very demanding on his women. Not the sort of man to be content with kisses and cuddles. She flushed at the line her thoughts had taken. Fabian Blackthorne's virility was no concern of hers.

'Hullo, chick,' her father smiled, coming up to the patio to fetch pruning shears and his basket. 'Have a nice day?'

'Not bad. Kaspar sends his regards.'

'Send him mine back. I'm just going to cut some nice roses for tomorrow night.

'Tomorrow night?' she queried.

'Yes.' He wandered down into the sunken rose-garden.

'I've invited someone to dinner tomorrow night.'

'Good,' she smiled. 'Who?'

'Friend of yours. Fabian Blackthorne.'

'*What?*' Cathy blinked in amazement, thinking she must have misheard him. 'Fabian? *Here?*'

'Thought it was time you had some company of your own age.' Her father's voice floated up from where he was invisibly cropping blooms from a bed of Sympathy. 'You haven't seen any of your friends for months.'

Cathy gaped, feeling like a fish that had been suddenly scooped on to the bank. 'B-but you *can't*,' she stammered. 'I—I'm going out, anyway——'

'You told me distinctly that you'd be in tomorrow night.' Her father's aristocratic face appeared over the roses to peer at where she was sitting on the garden swing-chair. 'I've told Blackthorne you'll be here. He's looking forward to meeting you.' Sir Cedric disappeared again, except for his hat, which was visible above the glossy green leaves. Cathy watched it in dismay. A bare week had passed since that disastrous evening at Mala's.

'For *dinner?*' she repeated, stunned.

'Thought you might make that Greek lamb thing. And one of your trifles to follow. We've still got some of that Château d'If, haven't we?'

'I don't know,' she said faintly. The prospect of entertaining Fabian, facing him over her own dinner-table, had left her speechless.

Stopping over a flower-laden Virgo shrub, Sir Cedric was smiling contentedly, obviously pleased with himself. It dawned on her that he'd made a point of inviting Fabian for *her* sake.

'*Daddy!* This isn't some attempt of yours to match me off, is it?'

'I don't know what you mean,' he said, but managed to look guilty and smug at the same time.

'You mustn't *do* things like this!' Cathy protested in exasperation. 'Why didn't you *ask* me before you went and invited Fabian?'

'He's a very fine lawyer,' he said, raising his eyebrows. 'You said you were friendly with him. In fact, I had an idea you were quite keen on the man.' He searched her troubled eyes. 'I had no idea there was any ill-feeling between the two of you.'

'Oh, there isn't.' She sighed, forcing a smile. 'I didn't mean to snap at you. It was just—a little sudden, that's all.'

'He's keen to see my rose-garden, you see.' The wistful look was still there. Her father loved showing his precious roses off to anyone who would pretend an interest. 'I was looking forward to showing him round. But if you want me to cancel the whole affair, I'll say I've been taken ill——'

'Oh no, don't do that. I was just a little startled because——' She hesitated, wondering whether now was the time to tell her father the whole sordid tale of her brush with *Caprice*. But she couldn't bring herself to do it. 'Oh well, I don't know why. It'll be nice to have someone around the house for a change.'

'That's exactly what I thought,' he nodded. 'I'm going to make an arrangement of some of my best roses for the dinner-table. I love to show them off.'

'I know.'

'And I'll get Mrs Matthews to give the dining-room a good going-over. Since you and I started eating in the kitchen, the dining-room hardly gets used any more.'

'Good idea.' Cathy was nodding absently as her father chattered on, snipping at his roses. 'I'd better get over to the hospital, Dad—I'm due there in a few minutes.' She gulped a cup of tea down in the kitchen, and went back to her car. Having acknowledged Fabian's powerful appeal for her, the thought of his coming to dinner wasn't exactly welcome. It filled her with a mixture of dread and excitement that was very disturbing. There would always be between them an unspoken tension that resulted from the spell he cast over her, and her own attraction towards him—and *Caprice*, and Cerise Hunniford and the fact that Fabian had seen her at her most vulnerable. A jagged mixture of good and bad things.

She drove across to the Addington, and taught for her regulation hour there. After a full day at Orientalia, the teaching session at the Addington was exhausting. The response she managed to get from the children, despite their brain damage or mental illness, was as electric as ever. Her theory about self-expression was being vindicated, it seemed. But tonight the effort drained her. She was quiet and thoughtful for the rest of the evening, her uneasy mind moving gingerly round the topic of Fabian, herself, and the redhaired Cerise Hunniford. In a mood of depression, it occurred to her that Cerise wasn't such an inappropriate partner for Fabian after all. She had the sex appeal, the sophistication, that he would demand from a woman. And unlike herself, she had the sharp good sense not to get herself into the sort of embarrassment Cathy had been through ...

The thought made her head for bed at an unusually early hour, feeling glum.

Despite her tiredness, though, sleep was elusive—and when it came, brought a jumble of released memories and dreams. The fragments of unwinding film resolved themselves slowly into a dream that grew frighteningly intense. She was on the roof of a tall building, pinned down by gunfire that was coming from she knew not where. Towering, glass-fronted skyscrapers loomed all round, and from some of the anonymous windows, people were machine-gunning her. As she clung to the concrete, exposed and utterly defenceless, she was aware of thousands of eyes watching her from the other windows; hungry, greedy eyes that devoured her, and yet refused to help. Eyes that enjoyed her terror, her nakedness.

And as she cowered in blind terror, trying to shut out the danger and the shame, something moved towards her. It resolved into a black jaguar, a vast, lithe cat of midnight black, red mouth wide.

A scream of fear rose silently in her throat as the jaguar closed in. She was staring into the beast's eyes; they were grey, commanding. Human eyes. She recognised them with a half-sob—Fabian's eyes. And then the black jaguar that loomed over her was transformed into Fabian, strong arms reaching for her. With a surge of relief she melted against him, nestling in his protective embrace.

The fact that he was naked did not, in her dream-logic, surprise her. The jaguar had worn no clothes, so it was obvious that Fabian wouldn't either. But now her dream changed shape and texture. His body was smooth and velvety as the jaguar's skin, his muscles sleek and powerful against her. He was smiling as he drew her upturned face slowly against his mouth. With unbearable sweetness, she felt his lips brush her temple, her cheeks, the corner of her mouth; his hands were hungry on her body, caressing, guiding her towards him.

And as her mouth yielded to the delicious tyranny of his kiss, her body opened to him, too. The strange thing was that this time she was glad, joyful—wanting it as urgently and as deeply as he. She heard his deep voice in her ear, felt his arms crushing her shoulders, clung to his taut muscles with trembling fingers. His body sank deep into hers, a shuddering power that swelled and filled her whole mind, her whole being . . .

'Fabian!' Gasping with the effort, she tore her way into wakefulness, and flung aside the bedclothes. All her smooth body was wet with perspiration, her heart pounding wildly. Unsettled and deeply disturbed, she padded through the darkness, tugging off her nightie, and threw the window wide on to the summer night. Her muscles were still quivering and weak, and she dragged the cool air gratefully into her hot lungs.

A crescent moon glowed in the deep blue sky like a golden horn. She lifted her arms to the cool night, feeling her full breasts ache as though a man's hands had indeed been caressing them roughly a few minutes ago.

Well, she thought wryly, no difficulty in explaining that dream, my girl. The threat of exposure in *Caprice*, Fabian's intervention—it was all as clear as daylight.

Except for the shuddering sexuality of the last few minutes. What would have happened had she not forced herself to wake up? Dream or premonition? The last erotic shadows of the dream still clung to her, isolated images that were powerful enough to tauten her nipples, make her catch her breath. She dismissed the thoughts angrily.

That her dream was more than partly wish-fulfilment didn't escape her. It just made her all the angrier at herself. She turned away from the peace of the night, and picked up her nightie. It was damp with sweat. Grimacing in self-mockery, she tossed it on to a chair and pulled a fresh one from her drawer.

Uneasily, she was aware that this dream had subtly deepened the way she felt about Fabian. She had tried to compartmentalise him, pack him neatly away in her mind. And he had burst out. Not the polite Fabian in his Savile Row suit—but the man inside the suit; the thrusting, virile man she had been unconsciously so aware of, even on their first meeting . . .

Sleep would be long in coming now, she knew that. In the darkness she remade her bed, then switched on the bedside lamp, and hunted for a book. She came up with a *Bunty Annual*, a battered favourite from her childhood. For some reason it appealed to her, and for the first time in what felt like decades, she paged through the book, losing herself in the comfort of the drawings, already old-fashioned-looking, their humour from a distant past of innocence.

The tap on her door came as no surprise. Her father had been a light sleeper since his attack, and she must have cried out in her sleep.

'Chick? All right?' His bony face poked round the door, silver hair ruffled.

'I'm fine,' she smiled tenderly, laying down the book. He came into the room, tugging his satin dressing-gown close around his spare frame. He stared at her with eyes that were, she realised with a start, becoming misty.

'What is it, Daddy?' she asked in dismay. 'Something wrong?'

'Just you,' he said gently. 'You've got the *Bunty Annual* out again.'

'Yes,' she nodded, surprised. 'Why "again"? I haven't looked at it for years.'

'I know.' He sat down on the end of her bed, his mouth still showing emotion. 'You don't remember, I suppose. But whenever you'd had a nightmare as a little girl, you used to switch on your light, and read that book. I used to see your light come on, and come and peep in at you—and there you'd be, sitting up in bed, that book on your lap, with your pigtails sticking straight out. You used to say, "I had a nightmare, Daddy." I suppose the book was a sort of security blanket for you.' He patted her legs. 'But you were a brave girl. You never woke your mother or me when you were frightened at night. You'd just get your *Bunty Annual* out and comfort yourself.' She watched him, so aware of his love for her that a lump had grown in her throat.

'Did I do that often?'

'As often as most children have nightmares, I suppose.' He smiled. 'If we found you asleep with your

Bunty Annual in the mornings, we'd know you'd had a bad dream.' His eyes were clever, loving. 'What was this one about?'

'I can't remember,' she lied awkwardly.

'It used to be lions and tigers in the jungle,' he mused, still watching her. 'Cathy, I've been an M.P. for nigh on twenty years. You get to know a bit about life in that time; I don't think I'm easily shocked. You've been very miserable lately, chick, and I suspect it's more than that feller Tim finding a new flame. Won't you tell me what it is?'

'Maybe some day,' she promised with a gulp. 'But not right now, Dad. I'm still trying to make sense of it all.'

'Okay.' He rose to kiss her resoundingly on the forehead. 'Don't read too late. You don't want to have shadows under your eyes for Fabian Blackthorne.'

'No,' she agreed drily.

'Goodnight, precious.'

'Goodnight, Dad.'

He closed the door. Cathy hugged the book absently, leaning her cheek against its smooth, cool cover. And thought of many things.

CHAPTER FOUR

As her father leaned back in his chair, rocking with laughter at something Fabian had said, Cathy realised with a pang how seldom, over the past four years, she had heard her father laugh like this. Fabian, his smoky grey eyes alight with amusement, turned to her.

'What's working for Kaspar Aprahamian like, Cathy?'

'Fascinating,' she said simply, 'Are you interested in Oriental carpets?'

'I'm interested in all things beautiful. Kaspar's one of the great authorities in the field. You must be quite an expert, then?'

'Oh, Cathy's a connoisseur,' Sir Cedric put in. 'Like you, she loves beauty, Fabian. Anything to do with art or sculpture is her field—but carpets are her speciality.'

'Indeed.' Fabian sipped the ruby wine thoughtfully, his eyes studying Cathy. The lamplight traced the contours of the bones in his face, emphasising the harshness, even arrogance, of his features. In gentler lights Fabian's face, with its broad forehead and high cheekbones, seemed to have a veneer of sophistication that somehow gentled him. But the eighteenth-century lamps in the dining-room somehow brought out an underlying, almost pagan quality in his face.

Or was that just an after-effect of her dream? Any way she looked at him, though, there was a brooding power about the level eyes and passionate mouth that made her suspect that his apparent relaxation was about as deceptive as the apparent immobility of a taut steel spring.

'I've worked for Kaspar for the past two years,' she said, trying to be more communicative with an effort. 'I've always loved carpets, you see—my mother used to collect them.' She glanced quickly at her father. 'She

63

took most of the best ones with her when she left.'
There was a little pause, her father looking absent-eyed
into his glass. 'I loved the patterns and the colours, even
when I was a little girl. I started buying them as soon as
I had any money of my own—and from then it was
natural to gravitate towards Kaspar. It was very kind of
him to offer me such a responsible job, especially when
I was so young. And I've picked up a great deal in the
time I've been with him.'

'I see,' mused Fabian. His eyes were thoughtful,
clever. 'You never wanted to do anything else?'

She looked down at her place. 'Such as what?'

'University,' he suggested. 'From what I've seen of
you, you have an excellent mind. You could go a long
way.'

Cathy simply shrugged, unwilling to embark on the
slightly sore point of her education.

'I have myself to blame for that, Fabian,' her father
said gently. 'You see, at about the time that Cathy left
school, my wife and I were breaking up. You know a
fair bit of the story already.' Fabian nodded. 'It hit
Catherine hard, I'm afraid. At that age it was bound to.
She was enrolled at university already, but somehow it
didn't work out, and she left in the first month, and
went to work. Against my wishes, I should say. I've
tried to persuade her to go back since then, but——'

'I simply didn't have the concentration,' Cathy said
quietly, meeting Fabian's thoughtful eyes. 'Daddy
blames himself, but that isn't true. I was too young for
university, that's all. And I enjoy working with Kaspar.
Perhaps I'll go back to university one day—but I still
don't feel I'm ready.'

'You're twenty-one,' said Fabian, and she nodded.
He leaned back in his chair, toying with his wineglass
with long, strong fingers. 'Art's a great comforter, isn't
it?'

She stared at him in surprise, nodding. By that
remark, he had shown he understood more about her
than she had imagined he could. She *had* taken refuge
in the beautiful world of rugs, finding solace in the

abstract beauty of their patterns as a prisoner might find solace in a tranquil view from a window. 'Yes,' she said slowly, 'art is a great comforter.'

'So is love.' He smiled directly into Cathy's eyes, melting her bones. 'My grandfather was in Persia in the early part of this century, and he collected quite a few rugs and carpets. Some of them are lovely, but I wouldn't know whether they're really valuable or not. Perhaps you'd come and take a look at them some time?'

'Oh! I don't have much spare time,' Cathy temporised hastily.

'And we could also have that game of squash we promised each other.'

Damn the man, she thought, feeling the powerful tug of her need for him. What was this—a come-on? Wasn't he content with Cerise Hunniford, must he also add her to his harem?

'I'm busy,' she said shortly.

'Don't be so graceless, Cathy,' Sir Cedric reproved, glancing from his daughter to the dark man with wise, glinting eyes. 'If Fabian wants advice on his carpets, I'd be glad to think you were paying back the Blackthornes for all the help they've given this family over the past half-century.'

'Well,' Cathy all but groaned, looking daggers privately at her father, 'I suppose I could just take a look . . .'

'Excellent,' Fabian said calmly. 'When are you free?'

'Monday afternoon?' she suggested, her unwillingness painfully obvious. She tossed back her cloud of dark hair, and rose to begin clearing the table before Fabian could agree or disagree. Ever since he had arrived, she had felt as though she were walking on eggshells. What was there about him to make her as nervous as a cat in a strange house? She would only be truly happy when he had gone. How late would he stay? Not later than ten, surely!

She stacked the plates on the sideboard, glancing covertly at Fabian and her father, who were discussing carpets. Fabian was more casually dressed tonight than she had yet seen him. The fine silk shirt he wore clung to the sculpted muscles of his shoulders and arms; and in deference to the warmth of the night, he had unbuttoned his collar to reveal the base of his powerful throat. Her eyes strayed to the gold medallion that glinted among the raven-black hair on his chest, not quite out of sight behind the silk. How elegant his hands were, yet how strong; they fascinated her, hands that could crush as well as caress, hands that could have been a surgeon's or a warrior's.

'We've been following your exploits lately,' Sir Cedric was saying. 'You argued brilliantly, if I may say so.'

'You mean the Massey case?' He looked up at Cathy, his tanned face amused. 'I didn't know you were interested in law, Cathy.'

'I'm not,' she said firmly. She had, in fact, made a conscious effort not to interest herself in the newspaper report which her father had shown her that morning, dealing with an industrial compensation case which Fabian had just won.

'I was very pleased with the outcome,' her father told her. 'I felt you had right on your side, and it was nice to know that the judges agreed.'

'Yes. The plaintiff had been shamefully treated,' Fabian said. 'His illness clearly was caused by the work he did at the factory. Their safety standards were far too lax—with the result that Albert Massey's life was all but destroyed. His first claim for compensation was crushed, principally because he had to conduct his own case, and he was no match for the clever lawyers that Williams Industrial hired. They tried the same arguments at the re-hearing, but it didn't take them long to see that the game was up. Williams were made to pay heavy compensation.'

'And you collected a nice fat fee,' Cathy put in coldly, somehow irritated by her father's obvious respect for Fabian's work.

'Cathy!' her father remonstrated, but Fabian merely smiled, armour-plated as ever.

'Actually, I took on the Massey case out of conviction. Not as a business proposition. Massey was *in forma pauperis.*'

'I don't understand Latin,' Cathy said coolly.

'*In forma pauperis* means that the defendant was too poor to pay legal fees,' her father explained. 'Fabian took on the case for nothing.'

'Oh,' said Cathy, reddening and turning away.

'Not for nothing,' Fabian smiled. 'I got a great deal of personal satisfaction out of the case. Our work is mostly rather dull—if you'll excuse me saying that to a most esteemed client. It was a great relief to get back into the courtroom.'

'You enjoy the struggle?'

'Immensely.' He glanced at Cathy. 'More than that, I happen to feel very strongly about the way huge institutions try and push helpless individuals around. And that applies to ruthless trade unions, ruthless bosses, ruthless governments—or any other powerful and faceless corporation that sets out to tell people what they can or can't do.'

'I couldn't agree more,' Sir Cedric nodded gently.

'Daddy's always been involved in fighting for the freedom of the individual,' Cathy put in, without meaning to have spoken.

'I know,' nodded Fabian. 'Your father's been on more committees that I care to count. And the legislation he sponsored on medical ethics,' he said, looking seriously into Cathy's eyes, 'is, in my opinion, one of the most important blows for individual liberty in the past twenty-five years.'

'That's very kind of you to say so,' Sir Cedric said. His spine had stiffened, and Cathy took his hand, inwardly in turmoil—what Fabian had said had delighted her, but she didn't want him to see it! 'Like you, I feel strongly about the way corporations bully little men and women. Now that I come to think of it,' he went on thoughtfully, 'weren't you involved in a similar case some time last year, Fabian? Something about the misuse of computers?'

'I'm surprised you remembered,' Fabian nodded. 'Yes, the Davies case, it wasn't exactly big news at the time.'

'But important, nonetheless.' The politician stroked his chin, eyes half-closed in thought. 'The principle was that computerised information about an individual's private life shouldn't be passed between companies, if I remember rightly.' Fabian nodded. 'And that case was also *in forma pauperis*.'

'Yes.'

'I didn't realise you were so benevolent,' Cathy said dryly, finding herself now having to fight down her growing admiration for Fabian Blackthorne. 'Do you do a lot of this sort of thing?'

'A fair bit. The Legal Aid Society know my interests, and they frequently ask me to take on these difficult cases.'

'But they don't turn out to be so difficult after you've taken them on?' she asked, almost trying to nettle him.

'I'm afraid that's not true,' he said quietly. 'Giant-killing is no easy task. I lose more cases than I care to think of at nights. But the very hopelessness of defending the individual against big business is the best reason I know for taking on the struggle.'

'You shouldn't knock Fabian,' her father said gently. 'He's doing a good job.'

And despite herself, Cathy found that she was inwardly agreeing with her father's assessment. Fabian was no comfortable business lawyer. One look at that clean-cut face, honed down to the epitome of male aggression, told you that. And those damnably sharp, disconcerting eyes—yes, she could well imagine that compelling power making even the most complacent bureaucrat uneasy.

In fact, she was going to have to beware of this growing respect for Fabian Blackthorne! He wasn't a man to treat lightly. And it was very unlikely indeed that he hadn't sensed by now that he affected her in a most direct way. Even by snapping at him like that, she had betrayed her feelings all too well. She rose.

'Coffee?' she offered unenthusiastically.

'I'd love some,' nodded Fabian, but her father glanced at his watch.

'It's getting late for an old invalid like me,' he sighed. I wonder if you'll excuse me, Fabian? You'll be quite safe with Cathy.'

'Daddy,' Cathy protested in dismay, 'you don't usually go to bed this early——'

'I'm feeling rather tired tonight,' he decided firmly. 'Look after Fabian, chick. Be sure to show him the port and cigars. It's been a pleasure having you here,' he said to Fabian, 'but I know you'll excuse me.'

Fabian rose to shake hands with the M.P., his grey eyes warm.

'Of course. It was a pleasure to be here, Sir Cedric. Perhaps when you're a little better you'll come to us at Blanchlands?'

'That's a date,' he promised, releasing the younger man's hand. He kissed Cathy goodnight, oblivious to her reproachful expression, and sailed serenely up to bed, leaving her alone with Fabian.

'I'm not going to eat you,' smiled Fabian, an ironic glint in his eyes. 'Why are you so afraid of me, Cathy?'

'I'm not afraid of you at all,' she retorted, the coolness in her voice covering anxiety. 'Perhaps you'd like to bring your coffee through to the drawing-room?'

Without waiting for his reply, she stalked off ahead. She didn't like being alone with him.

He leaned against the doorway, watching her. The cool shirt and tight black slacks that hugged his hips and thighs emphasised the blade-like quality of his body disturbingly. His expression was quizzical.

'You don't like me much, do you?'

'Whatever makes you say that?' she enquired drily.

'At Mala's party you gave me the impression that you weren't exactly unwilling to explore our relationship further,' he said softly. 'Tonight you've been treating me like the princess to the peasant. What's changed your mind so dramatically?'

'Perhaps you were mistaken at Mala's party.' She

glanced back coolly into the grey eyes. 'In my experience, men flatter themselves vastly over their appeal for the opposite sex.'

'Indeed?' he grinned, even white teeth glinting against the dusky bronze of his skin. 'That's a rather cynical viewpoint. And yet I'm sure I wasn't mistaken. I hope you didn't take Cerise Hunniford's little piece of bitchery too seriously?'

'Seriously?' She was cold with anger as she thrust her father's favourite box of cigars at him. 'It was intended seriously enough.' She tried to bite back the words, but they burst out nevertheless: 'She was being as spiteful as she possibly could, and you know it.'

'I wouldn't enter her in a Nice Person competition,' Fabian said mildly. 'But you didn't give her much of a chance, either.'

'Why should I?' Cathy demanded. 'I can't imagine what you see in her,' she went on, aware that she was in danger of exposing her sharp jealously. 'She's hard and crude. She just uses people.'

'Cerise is an interesting person,' he said, his eyes amused. 'And she has a soft centre, despite her hardness.'

'I'll bet,' Cathy muttered.

'You're too harsh with her,' smiled Fabian, inspecting the cigars. 'She has a great deal to recommend her.'

'I can imagine the assets which recommend her to *you*,' she retorted.

'Now who's being spiteful?' He rolled a cigar under his nose, aquiline nostrils flaring as he inhaled the fine bouquet. Cathy snapped the box shut, looking as though she wished his fingers had been in it. 'Cerise is just a businesswoman,' he said. 'Why despise her for that?'

'Because her *business*, as you call it, is despicable. Oh, I know there are plenty of useful euphemisms for what she sells—"glamour" is what they call it, don't they?' She twisted her mouth scornfully, her jade-green eyes bright with anger. 'It's sexual exploitation, pure and simple. But perhaps that excites you!'

'Is it?' He lit his cigar with a table-lighter, and exhaled a long plume of the blue smoke upwards. 'Well, you ought to know.'

Furiously, Cathy swung her hand at his face, but his arm was swiftly in the way, blocking the slap in mid-air. His free arm curled around her waist with the speed of a whip, and slammed her against him so that his taut thighs and stomach muscles rammed against her body.

'Let me go!' she spat in a fierce whisper.

'You're too spoiled for your own good,' he growled, sparks of anger igniting in his own eyes. 'Your piety becomes you, Catherine Milner. But is it real?'

'Bastard,' she hissed, 'I'll scream for my father!'

'Go ahead,' he invited. She was burningly aware of his hard body through the thin cotton of her skirt, and the scarlet rushed to her cheeks as she thrust frantically against his broad chest. She might as well have tried to push over a hundred-year oak. Staring down at her thoughtfully, he puffed at his cigar, letting the acrid smoke drift from between his lips, his dark eyes narrowed.

'"Pornography",' he said, his deep voice calm, 'is an ancient Greek word referring to the messages that the ladies of the night used to leave on walls. Advertisements, shall we say, for custom.'

'You're hurting me,' she pleaded, half intoxicated by his power and his proximity. Oh, his body was so strong, so hard! Tim had never felt like this, never. Fabian's body was alien, overwhelmingly male. The harsh contact between them was eroding her self-control, dissolving her will, seeming to make her melt inwardly . . .

'In a way, that definition isn't inappropriate these days, is it, Cathy?'

'What do you mean?' she demanded, struggling futilely against him.

'I mean that what you did—posing for those pictures—might just be construed as a sort of advertisement.'

'That's crazy!'

'It could almost be called a signal.' His face was brooding, his eyes burning into hers. 'A signal that you wanted the kind of attention those photographs hinted at.'

'*No!*' she exclaimed furiously. 'The whole thing was a horrible mistake——'

'I find that very hard to believe,' he said ominously.

'I don't care what you believe! I'm not the sort of woman you think!'

'No?' Fabian let another long feather of thick smoke drift out of his lips. His mouth held dark passion. 'It's an interesting question. You're a very beautiful woman, Cathy,' he said softly. 'Your skin's as fine as satin, and your mouth is positively exquisite.' She stared up at him, hypnotised by the caressing sexuality of his deep voice. 'Green eyes and black hair—a very potent combination. You shouldn't have to advertise for men.'

'I didn't,' she protested frantically, shaking her head. 'You don't understand—you don't know what happened——'

'Perhaps you ought to tell me.'

'It's none of your damned business!'

His eyes narrowed. 'I intend to make it my business, Cathy.' He flicked the cigar through the french doors, its coal like a shooting star in the dark garden. Without releasing her, his right hand moved to the top button of her blouse and eased it open, revealing the cool white hollow of her slender throat. Though his fingers had barely grazed her skin, she shuddered uncontrollably, the blood draining from her cheeks.

'What are you going to do?' she breathed, her heart leaping into her throat. His face was merciless.

'I'm going to find out about you,' he said softly. 'All about you.' The next button slipped from its mooring, and now the gentle slope of her breasts was visible, her skin creamy against the lacy froth of her bra.

'*Stop,*' she begged, her eyes closing as the caress of his fingers devastated her senses. A third button opened.

'I want to know why you went to the *Caprice* studio

that afternoon,' he said quietly. 'I want to know everything that happened before and after. Otherwise, my sweet Cathy——' his lips were warm against her temple, exactly as they had been in her dream, '—I'm going to simply assume that you're the sort of woman your actions say you are.' Her blouse was open to the waist now, and her brain seemed to be in the midst of a fire that raged through her entire being, consuming her in its heat. Through half-closed eyes she stared helplessly into the dark, cruel face above her, feeling his hands caress her shuddering flanks, slide up the skin of her back to find the catch of her bra.

'Fabian, for the love of God,' she moaned, 'don't do this——'

'Why not? You want it as much as I do, despite all your protestations. Don't you?' As the silky material slid away from her breasts, she gasped out loud. His mouth claimed hers with a raw passion that clawed her emotions, his fingers cupping her breast, expertly manipulating the rosebud peak into an aching star of desire. Feeling as though the whole centre of her being had dropped into space, she crumpled against him, surrendering to their torment, the ecstasy of what his body was doing to hers. *This is my dream*, her mind told her wildly, *this is what I've wanted, ever since I set eyes on this man* . . .

His mouth tasted of wine and cigars, invading her senses, thrusting her into an involuntary response. Scarcely knowing whether she was dreaming or waking, she let her fingers slide over the breadth of his shoulders. Oh, darling, her heart whispered to him, you're so warm! I never knew a man's skin could be so warm. I never knew . . . Her nipples were thrusting against his fingers, stiff with the urgency of meeting his touch, even as her body recoiled from the unbearable intensity of the sensation. It was as though her lips had fused with his, as though she were drinking Fabian's soul into her own, as though her body were opening like a flower to his sun-heat.

He tore his mouth away from hers, leaving her

shaking in his arms. They were breathing in unison now, fast and hard.

'Please,' she begged between gasps, 'let me go, Fabian——'

'We've been waiting for this from the first time we saw each other,' he said with a fierce smile. His eyes were hungry, devouring her face, her lips, her naked breasts. 'Why deny it? And I'm still waiting to hear your story, my sweet.' She closed her eyes in surrender, letting her head drop back so that her midnight-black hair cascaded away from her high forehead. 'Otherwise,' he promised, 'we'll pursue these entertainments to their logical conclusion—on that couch over there.'

With an effort, she opened her eyes to look at him through dewy lashes.

'You wouldn't,' she said in a soft gasp.

'I would. Believe me, Cathy—I would.' He slid his hands to her hips and pulled her forward hard against him, so that she could feel the dizzying thrust of his desire, hard and potent against her loins. 'You know I'm quite capable of doing exactly that,' he growled, his stormy eyes possessing her utterly. As though guessing that he had won his way, Fabian took her in his arms.

'Now,' he said softly, cradling her so that she could rest her aching head against his chest, 'tell me. Why did you go to the *Caprice* studio that day?'

CHAPTER FIVE

'I DIDN'T go there,' she said numbly. His skin was velvety warm against her cheek, the deep thud of his heart seeming to fill her soul. 'Not deliberately. I was simply passing by.' She drew a shaky breath. 'I don't know if you'd ever understand.'

'Try me.'

'Last week,' she began, falteringly, 'you—you said that there wasn't all that much to Tim Coryat. Well, maybe that's so. He was no superman. He was weak, not strong, not anything. But to me he was—oh, so important.'

'And you went to *Caprice* because you broke up with Tim?'

'In a way,' she said tiredly, 'yes.' Fabian was silent, listening to the dreamy murmur of her voice against his chest. 'When my mother walked out, I felt as though my whole world had collapsed. Everything I'd trusted, everything I'd taken for granted, just vanished overnight. And somehow, my whole faith in the world was shattered. I know it sounds naïve,' she said, her lips twisting as though she were tasting poison, 'but I kind of—well, almost *revered* Mummy. I'd always thought of her as a sort of angel. Thought she could do no wrong. In my fantasies, she was a fairy queen, and I was her princess. Can you understand what I mean?'

'I'm trying,' he said quietly.

'If that seems mawkish, just remember that I was barely seventeen at the time. A very innocent seventeen.'

Fabian grunted. 'Then what?'

'And then Tim came along. He was much older than me, but somehow that made him all the more protective, more reassuring. It was as though he held my life together. Daddy was remote, withdrawn. We

75

hardly ever saw each other in those days. But Tim was
there, secure, solid.'

'The Rock of Ages,' Fabian said drily. 'I didn't
realise you'd gone out with him for such a long
time.'

'It was over three years,' she sighed. 'I left school,
tried university, couldn't concentrate. I joined Kaspar,
and started learning about Oriental art. It was difficult
work, but I loved it.'

'And it was all hunky-dory.'

'No. No—that's when it all started becoming a
nightmare. Tim and I—we were never intimate. I—I
mean, we kissed and held hands and all that, but—
but——'

'You didn't let him make love to you.'

'No,' she said, almost inaudibly. 'I was too young,
for one thing. But after my eighteenth birthday, Tim
started wanting more and more. He said he'd waited for
two years, and now he wanted some proof that I loved
him. He said it was more or less my duty——'

'Charming,' Fabian grunted. 'I take it you were far
too moral, and were suitably shocked at this earthy
approach?'

'Mock me if you want to,' she said gently. 'I'm just
trying to explain how it was, Fabian. And no, it wasn't
that I was so moral. I had desires, like any other
woman. But somehow I couldn't respond to Tim. He
used to hurt me—he was clumsy, somehow *greedy*. I
just couldn't make myself like what he wanted. So it
always ended with me saying no, and usually bursting
into tears. Then there'd be a scene, and he'd call me
frigid, neurotic—he had a whole lot of names for me
when he was angry.'

'Men are cruel sometimes,' he said absently, his deep
voice surprisingly gentle. 'You're shivering. Let's have a
brandy inside while you tell me the rest of it.'

There were shadows under her beautiful emerald
eyes, he noticed as he poured brandy for them both,
and the hands with which she fastened her blouse were
shaking.

Cathy gulped at the brandy, choking as its fire sank into her stomach.

'It got worse and worse,' she said, talking compulsively now, as though Fabian had opened some floodgate inside her. 'He grew violent sometimes. And I was so depressed that I didn't know where to turn. If it hadn't been for Kaspar, and having to look after Daddy when he had his heart attack, I don't know what would have become of me.' She gulped again, grateful for the burning of the alcohol in her throat. 'I was very overwrought, on the edge of some kind of breakdown. And then I went round to Tim's flat one afternoon.' She closed her eyes, reliving the horror of what had happened. 'He wasn't expecting me. I was supposed to be at Kaspar's shop, but Kaspar had to go up to Edinburgh unexpectedly, and he gave me the day off. I had a key to the flat, and I thought I'd surprise Tim. So I just let myself in. Then I heard noises from the bedroom—like a fight, or a bad argument. I ran through to see what was happening.' She stopped, shuddering. Fabian was watching her intently, his eyes dark. He reached out a gentle hand to pat her knee.

'Take it easy, Cathy. What was going on in the bedroom?'

'Tim—Tim was in there, with another woman. The place was like——' she gulped, 'like a torture-chamber. He was tied up, and she was whipping him—and he was screaming——' She broke off, unable to go on. He was beside her quickly, his strong arms gentling her, his protective warmth around her. She clung to him, the man-smell of him seeming to ease away the horror of her memories.

'I couldn't believe it. I thought it was for real at first, that this was some kind of terrible attack. But then I realised. They were wearing these horrible clothes, and she'd brought——' Cathy paused, not wanting to remember, 'things—disgusting, perverted things. He saw me,' she went on, her voice muffled against his shoulder. 'The woman started laughing, saying that I should have done this for Tim, that she'd had to do it for years because I hadn't. She said that if I had he wouldn't have needed to go to her. I ran out, but he came after me, and stopped me at the door. He was excited that I'd seen him like that. He wasn't like the Tim I knew at all—he was like a complete stranger, frightening and horrible.' She stopped, aware that Fabian had made her say things she'd sworn to herself never to tell anyone. 'Fabian—for God's sake, promise you'll never breathe a word of this.'

'I promise,' he said quietly. 'What happened?'

'He said, "Now you know", and I said, "Yes." He wanted me to come and join what—what they were doing in the bedroom. And when I started crying, he flew into a rage. The woman was standing there, laughing and watching. Tim called me every name under the sun, cruel, wicked names. And then, at the end, he said it was all over between us. He said, "You're just ice from the waist down. You haven't got a spark of sex in you." And then I ran out.'

There was a long pause. Fabian rocked her in his arms, his face set. Cathy allowed herself to just rest against him, losing herself in his protection.

'You shouldn't have had to go through that,' he said slowly. 'He should have told you long ago. But it's all over now. What did you do after that?'

'I got into my car.' She thought hard. 'There was a bottle of whisky with my shopping, a twelve-year-old malt that I was going to give to Daddy. I was in a wild state, crying and shaking—and I just sat there, drinking from the bottle. And then, when my feelings were numbed, I started to drive home.'

'That's when you passed the *Caprice* studios.'

'Yes. This sign outside caught my eye—they wanted models. And what Tim had said came into my mind— that I was ice, that no man wanted a virgin saint. So I had this crazy idea that I'd show them just how hot I could be. I wanted to—oh, I don't know. To get some kind of revenge on Tim, on me, on the whole world.' She looked up at him with troubled eyes. 'Can you understand that?'

'I think so,' he smiled gently. 'But that mood wore off.'

'Very fast,' she winced. 'Suddenly, I couldn't remember what I was trying to prove any more—and the whole thing began to hit me. I grabbed my clothes and ran out. But by then, of course, it was too late— much too late.' She pulled out of his arms, and walked slowly back to the french doors, staring with dulled eyes into the night. 'So. Now you've found out what you wanted to know,' she went on, her voice low. 'Are you satisfied?'

'Partly.'

She turned to him with a bitter little smile. 'Only partly? You're not an easy man to satisfy. What did you do that to me for, Fabian? Why was it so important to you that you half raped me to find out what you wanted?'

'Just testing a theory.' His dark eyes met hers with a hint of their old mockery. 'I wanted to know whether you really were the nice little girl you seemed to be, or whether you were some kind of corrupt nymphet.'

'And what am I?' she challenged.

'I'm not sure, yet,' he confessed. He rose to his feet, lithe and very masculine. 'You're very young, that's for sure.'

'Yes,' she said drily, 'I notice you prefer the older woman. Tell me something—is Cerise your lover?'

His grey eyes, fringed with thick, dark lashes surveyed her dispassionately.

'That's none of your business,' he replied calmly.

'God,' she hissed, 'you've got a damned nerve! How come the most intimate secrets of *my* life are *your* business, then?'

'Because I'm the family lawyer,' he said silkily. 'It's my business to know all the family secrets.'

'I see,' she retorted through gritted teeth. 'Then I take it this evening has been just a fact-finding tour for you? And what you did to me out there—that was simply your way of getting a look at the skeletons in my closet?'

'Partly,' he admitted without a trace of guilt. 'It was also rather delicious.'

'Not to me,' she snapped, angered at his arrogance.

'No? You're lying, Cathy.'

'And you're vain,' she retorted.

'The point is easily proved,' he purred. He was dazzlingly handsome, as handsome as Lucifer, and she swayed as he took her face between warm hands.

She closed her eyes as he leaned forward to kiss her; but this time the onslaught was not the savage torment she had known before. This time his lips were so exquisitely gentle that she almost cried out. His tongue traced the outline of her lips with lingering desire, dipping against her teeth, tasting the inner sweetness of her mouth.

'My Cathy,' he whispered, his breath mingling warm and intimate with her own, 'if you really don't want this, all you have to do is step away.'

It was true; his hands against her face were as light as a breeze, her tingling body not even touching his. All she had to do was step back. But the kiss she was sinking into was a paradise she couldn't forgo. The caress of his mouth deepened, became a sweet flame that took possession of her soul. And her body, aching for the feel of him, was reaching forward of its own accord, her arms sliding round his neck, her breasts pressing to his chest, her hips moving forward at first shyly, then urgently, to meet the bone-melting power of his desire.

And it was Fabian who stepped back, leaving her accused by her own body.

'You see? You want this exactly as much as I do,' he said softly. Cathy covered her burning face with her fingers, unable to reply to his taunt. Then she let her hands hang limp at her sides.

'Why don't you play these games with Cerise Hunniford?' she asked dully. 'She'll give you a better match, Fabian. After all, I'm only an amateur.'

'A very talented amateur,' he smiled, drawing one finger down her pale cheek. 'It's time you were in bed, Cathy Milner. Walk me to my car.'

Silently, she walked beside him down to where his white Daimler was parked on the driveway.

'I don't want to see you again, Fabian,' she told him, twisting her hands. His laugh was genuinely amused.

'Don't be silly—this is just getting interesting. Besides, we have an appointment on Monday afternoon. You're coming to assess Grandfather's carpets—remember? I'll pick you up from Kaspar's shop. Say five-thirty?'

'I won't be there,' she rejoined.

'Oh yes, you will.' Fabian kissed her cool lips. 'You'll be there, all right.'

She watched the red tail-lights disappear into the night, the warmth of his smile branded into her mind. Then she turned and walked back to the house, feeling bruised all over.

Why in God's name was she so susceptible to him? She was too tired to think. She felt like a pool that had been so troubled and shaken that the bottom was no longer clear; Fabian Blackthorne had torn through her defences in a way that no man or woman had ever done before.

Aching for sleep, she tiptoed past her father's bedroom. But he was awake.

'All right, sweetie?'

'Fine, Dad,' she called softly. 'See you in the morning. Sleep well.'

'Sleep well, chick.'

The moon glowed in at the window, fuller than last night, more golden. Waxing, she thought dreamily. Growing and preparing. But for what?

'If I were a beautiful young woman,' said Kaspar Aprahamian, 'and a very handsome, influential young man was coming to pick *me* up——' gently, he pinched Cathy's cheek '—I would at least be wearing a smile.'

'Fabian makes me very uncomfortable.' Cathy sighed as she heaved a Kurdestan rug into a more prominent place, and glanced at the clock again. It was five-thirty-two. 'And I don't exactly relish spending an evening with him and his grandfather's plundered treasures.'

'Strange. To me he seems an ideal friend for you.'

'*Friend?*' Cathy shook her head at the Armenian. 'You're just like my father, Kaspar—always trying to mate me off with some glamour boy. You mean "husband", don't you?'

'I meant what I meant,' the old man replied with dignity. There was a twinkle in his wizened face, though. 'Besides, your father is right. It *is* time you started thinking of settling down and raising a family.'

'I'm only just twenty-one,' Cathy retorted.

'My mother was sixteen when I was born.' He, too, glanced up at the clock. 'Time to shut the shop. Your young man is late, it seems.' He made his way up the stairs to lock the shop door, moving with the caution of the brittle-boned elderly. Cathy watched him with affection. Kaspar and her father, two men who had given her so much kindness, so much strength to lean on. Both now growing visibly older, visibly more worn and frail.

'If he's not here in five minutes, I'm taking the Tube home,' Cathy promised grimly, and heard Kaspar's chuckle from up the stairs.

'"Expectation is the sauce of love", my dear. Perhaps Mr Blackthorne is caught in the rush-hour traffic.'

'Or perhaps he's trying to whet my appetite for his company,' she retorted. It would be just like Fabian's arrogance to make her wait, to remind her how firmly he was in command. Again, nerves twisted in her stomach at the thought of being in his company that evening. No matter how she resisted him intellectually, her deepest instincts responded to Fabian in a way that she could never hope to control. Okay, she muttered to herself, so he's exciting, an expert seducer. Does that mean you have to start off like a doe every time his image comes up in your mind? And just because he's a brilliant lawyer with strong ideals, do you have to stand in such awe of him? He's only a man, after all . . .

Her beautiful mouth set in a determined line, she hauled some more carpets into line. It had been a good day; she and Kaspar had sold some of their finest rugs to favourite customers. It was now twenty to six. Kaspar was standing absently at the door, staring out into the busy street with dim eyes. What was he thinking of? His first love, so many years ago in Armenia?

'It's getting late, Kaspar,' she called. 'Why don't you get off home? I'll wait for his lordship here, and lock up when I leave.'

'Perhaps you're right,' he nodded, turning back to come down the stairs. 'It's been a busy day, and——'

The telephone chirruped beside Cathy, and she grimaced at Kaspar. 'That, no doubt, will be Fabian with some unlikely excuse.' She picked up the receiver, trying to pretend a casualness she was far from feeling, while Kaspar watched her face with a half-smile. 'Yes?'

'Cathy?' It was her father, his voice leaden.

'What is it, Dad? Are you all right?'

'I've got some bad news for you,' he said heavily. 'About Fabian Blackthorne.'

An arctic chill closed round her heart, seeming to freeze the warm blood in her veins. She listened in numb horror to what he had to tell her, answering only in monosyllables, and when she replaced the receiver, her face was bone-white.

'For God's sake, what is it?' the old man asked.

'There's been an accident,' she whispered, as though scarcely able to believe her own words.

'Fabian?' he guessed anxiously.

'Yes.' Strangely, no tears would come. 'That was my father. There was a car crash this afternoon. Fabian's in Guy's Hospital—he's in the intensive care unit.'

'Then he's alive? Praise be to God!'

'He's in a deep coma,' she said dully. Kaspar's face sagged in tired pain, and he reached out both hands to her. She took them, thinking with cold pain that the old man's fingers had lost their strength, their power to comfort. 'They don't know if he's going to pull through.' She roused herself fighting through the tragic emptiness inside her heart. 'I must go to the hospital at once, Kaspar.'

'I'll drive you there now,' he nodded, still looking stunned.

'Fabian's father will be there by now. With no one to look after him.' She shook her head, looking at Kaspar with blind, tear-blurred eyes. The futility of injury and death had taken on an unbearable clarity for her. 'A drunk ran into his car at an intersection. Isn't that silly? Isn't that the silliest thing you ever heard?'

With distant surprise, Cathy realised that she hadn't eaten a thing all day. The atmosphere of a late-night hospital sat heavily over the day-room. Nervous strain and exhaustion had left dark smudges under Cathy's eyes, but hope still lurked somewhere inside her.

'He's so strong.'

Cathy glanced up at Keith Blackthorne, huddled on the bench beside her. Fabian's father had obviously once been a strong man. Now, shocked and exhausted, old age had suddenly caught up with him. She had given him what comfort she could over the past few hours, and in a strange way they had passed from being strangers to friends. 'He's so strong,' Keith Blackthorne said again, studying his clasped hands as though he might find the answer to his son's life there. 'Even as a boy. He was always smiling, always so cheerful. When his mother died, he took it so bravely. He'll come through—he must!'

'Of course he will,' she said comfortingly. But she knew that the specialist's grim warning was haunting him as much as her——

'The only hope in these cases is immediate action. He's being prepared for an operation right now. But even if we succeed in stopping the haemorrhage, there may already be serious brain damage.'

'What does that mean?' Keith Blackthorne had asked in a shaken voice.

'It's a lot too early to say. We'll have a much clearer picture after the operation.' The specialist's austere face hadn't softened. He was a technician, a highly-skilled brain surgeon who simply couldn't afford emotional

involvement, the concession to feeling that might make
his knife falter among the precious tissues of the mind.
'If there's any damage to the motor region of the brain,
your son may not be the same man again.'

'You mean—paralysis?' Cathy had whispered.

'Perhaps. It's not impossible, I'm afraid. But we must
all keep our spirits up. That's the only way we'll be able
to help. I'll get one of the nurses to bring you some tea.'

Now, weary hours later, half a dozen empty teacups
stood on the melamine table in front of them. And
Fabian was still in the operating theatre, under the
surgeon's scalpel.

She had only once in all those hours allowed herself
to think about Fabian's death. The thought had torn at
her heart. If Fabian died, she knew she would be left in
an emotional desolation that would be very hard to
survive. Somehow, not even her father's brush with
death had affected her like this. Was that a shocking
thing to admit?

Whatever her feelings for Fabian, he was so alive, so
vivid with energy and creativity. It was almost
impossible to imagine him in any other condition—cold
in the earth, or imprisoned by a disability. Or worst of
all, the spectre that haunted Cathy's exhausted
imagination, reduced to the permanent vegetation of
the seriously brain-damaged. That, she knew, was the
meaning which lay behind the specialist's words. That
Fabian might become an uninhabited body, the vivid
light in those grey eyes extinguished for ever. Only the
heart, the lungs, the kidneys and liver, labouring
unwillingly to maintain a parody of life. Her fingernails
bit into her palms, dragging her mind away from the
brink of that horror.

As if sensing her thoughts, Keith Blackthorne turned
to her with a tired smile.

'I'll miss him, Cathy, if he dies. He's been a
wonderful son to me—caring and loyal. He's been
more—a true friend. And very few fathers can say that
about their sons.'

'He's been your partner for some years now, hasn't

he?' asked Cathy, trying to distract the grey-haired man from his worry.

'Seven years now,' he nodded. 'Since he was twenty-four. The everyday work of the office is probably far too dull for him—he's at his best in complicated, difficult cases. You probably know about the work he does for the Legal Aid Society?'

'I've heard,' she smiled. 'My father and I have been following one of his cases lately.'

'He's very good. He never proclaims his ideals, or anything like that—but he's got a deep conviction about justice for the individual. And he never backs down from any fight. He never has done.'

'Then he won't back down from this one,' Cathy said gently, laying her hand on Keith's wrinkled fingers. Gratefully, the old man clung to her hand, his eyes dim.

'Some people find him almost formidable,' he went on.

'Really?' Cathy smiled, with a touch of dryness.

'Yet he's so kind, so true. He does so much to help people who haven't got the money for legal advice of their own. The law isn't a profession in which you'll find much charity, Cathy. Fabian's a rare exception.' He smiled wryly as she nodded. 'I'm sorry. A proud father must be the most boring conversationalist in the world.'

'You've got reason to be proud,' she said gently. 'And I'm more than interested. What was he like as a boy?'

'Full of fun—frankly, quite wicked. His mother's death changed some of that, though ... When Mary died, he seemed suddenly to grow up.' Weariness sat heavy on Keith's lids. 'He was always a clever boy. Not brilliant at school—but he came into his own at university.'

'He got top grades?'

'Almost always,' he nodded. 'Which is amazing, considering his social life.'

'Lots of girl-friends, I suppose?'

Keith Blackthorne smiled, squeezing her hand.

'Nothing serious, I can assure you. Don't feel threatened.' Cathy flushed. How did he know about her sense of insecurity about Fabian? 'I didn't know it showed,' she said ruefully.

'It doesn't. But the two of you are sweet on each other, aren't you?'

'N-not exactly,' said Cathy, trapped by the awkward question.

'I was looking forward to meeting you tonight.' He glanced at his watch, the smile ebbing from his face. 'Dear heaven, why must these people drink and drive? If only they knew! If only they knew . . .'

'Don't think about it,' Cathy said gently. She hesitated, then put her arm around his shoulders. Gratefully, Keith leaned back against her supporting arm, his eyes closing heavily. Within minutes he was asleep, leaving Cathy to stare emptily ahead, alone with her fears and prayers.

How little we know of the future, she thought drearily. Maybe it's a blessing that we can't see what's in store for ourselves . . .

'Miss Milner?'

Cathy turned with a start to the middle-aged night nurse who had touched her shoulder. 'They're coming out of the theatre now.'

'Is he alive?' she asked urgently. Keith Blackthorne jerked into wakefulness, his eyes wild.

'He's alive,' she nodded. But her face was sombre. 'Mr Baker is coming to talk to you about the operation now.'

'Is my son going to be all right?' the old man demanded fearfully.

'The specialist will explain the situation exactly,' the nurse evaded, and looked relieved as the surgeon came into the day-room carrying a file. The past hours in the theatre had incised deep lines around his mouth and eyes, and his expression was drained. Cathy and Keith Blackthorne rose to meet him.

'How is my son?' the lawyer burst out. 'Is he going to live?'

'He should live,' the surgeon nodded. 'He's very very lucky. We managed to stem the broken artery that was flooding his brain.'

'Thank God!' the old man breathed. But Cathy had seen the same grim look in the surgeon's face as there had been in the nurse's.

'Has his brain——has it been damaged?' she asked.

'To some extent, yes.' Mr Baker ran his hand wearily through his hair, glancing at their terrified faces. 'As a matter of fact, he's semi-conscious now. The operation ended over an hour ago.' They waited for him to go on, neither able to ask the question. 'There has been some residual damage to your son's brain,' the surgeon went on, turning to Keith Blackthorne. 'The haemorrhage extended across the left side of the cortex. It's unlikely that any of his motor functions will be impaired. He'll be able to walk and talk perfectly. And as far as we can tell, his thought-centres are undamaged.'

'But?' whispered Cathy, giving a sound to the word that hovered in the air.

'But there's some doubt about his eyesight.' The dread in their faces made him grimace. 'Quite a lot of doubt, in fact. I have to say that the outlook is poor. The sight centre was invaded by blood in the first seconds after the impact. And I'm afraid that the damage is likely to be irrevocable.'

'Blind,' said Keith Blackthorne, almost conversationally. His face had the rigid expression of total shock. Cathy shook her head in bewilderment, her whole body flooded with the dead cold of a winter sea. 'Blind? That's impossible! It can't be true——'

'There's a chance that it may not be permanent,' the surgeon said gently. 'We won't be able to tell that for a long time to come. But we've already tested his eyes as far as possible, and he has no sight. The pupils don't react to light.'

'But—but can't anything be done?'

'That remains to be seen,' the surgeon hedged. 'It's possible that in the future, new techniques will be developed——'

'You mean there's nothing that can be done?' Keith Blackthorne asked in a shaking voice. 'You mean that my son will never see again?'

'That's a possibility we have to face—yes.' The surgeon paused, pinching the bridge of his nose with tightly-shut eyes. 'Yes, that's exactly what I mean, Mr Blackthorne.'

'A graft——' Cathy blurted out.

'There's nothing wrong with his eyes,' Mr Baker said, a tinge of exhausted irritation creeping into his precise voice. 'I've just tried to explain. The centre of sight in the brain has been damaged. There's absolutely nothing I or any of my colleagues can do right now.' More gently, he went on, 'I'm terribly sorry to have to be so pessimistic, but I must repeat that the outlook is not good. We did all we could. Maybe with time, some time in the future——' He shrugged.

'Can we see him?' asked Keith Blackthorne.

'Only for a few minutes. He won't be very coherent, and you mustn't disturb him. I'll get the nurse to take you to him.'

CHAPTER SIX

FABIAN was in an isolation ward, a drip attached to one arm, and an electronic device measuring vital data from wires attached to his chest. Cathy had her arm firmly through Keith Blackthorne's, supporting the elderly lawyer, whose legs seemed to be weak. The hush was broken only by the regular bleep of the cardiograph, measuring the slow pulse of life in the man who lay with closed eyes on the white pillows. In the soft light, his face had taken on an almost beautiful, ethereal quality, and Cathy found herself holding her breath, as if in a church. His skin was the colour of pale gold, and the powerful muscles of his shoulders and chest were relaxed in submission.

'Fabian?' his father whispered. 'Can you hear me, boy?' The heavy lashes fluttered, and Cathy watched, numb with grief, as his mouth tightened in pain.

'Dad?' Slowly, Fabian's eyes opened. With a sense of delayed shock, Cathy tried to make herself understand that those electrifying grey eyes were now sightless. For a few seconds they searched the room aimlessly, then closed wearily. 'They have to keep me in the dark,' he said, his voice made husky by the anaesthetic. 'Something to do with my eyes. I'm all right, Dad— honestly.'

'Sure you are,' the old man said, his own eyes wet. He reached out a wrinkled hand to pat his son's shoulder. 'Sure you are, boy. You'll be out of here in no time.' He broke off, trying to control his voice. Cathy, on the brink of tears herself, was finding it terrible to see Fabian lying there, unaware of what had happened to him. That sense of tragedy was almost unbearably strong now, threatening to destroy her fragile poise altogether.

'Fabian?' she said gently. 'Can you hear me?'

'Cathy.' A smile flickered across his mouth. 'Sorry about this evening. I was looking forward to showing you Grandad's spoils. Some other time, maybe.'

'Some other time,' she agreed. She could feel Keith Blackthorne's grief, and somehow the need to comfort him kept her from breaking down herself. 'The nurse is signalling us to leave now,' she said, glancing up through the observation window. 'I—we'll come and see you tomorrow.'

'Good,' he replied. Cathy could see him drifting back into unconsciousness, his face relaxing. 'Maybe they'll have the lights on by then,' he murmured.

Instinctively, she stooped over him, and touched his lips with her own. They were cold, but his faint smile told her he knew what she had done. With a last glance at his face, she drew the old man gently out.

Outside the ward, he stood bowed with grief for a long time and then slowly straightened up. His face was gaunt.

'I'm sorry,' he said mechanically. 'Silly of me. Saw plenty of that sort of thing in the last war—but somehow, seeing my own boy like that——' He broke off, swaying on his feet. The night nurse took his shoulders quietly and nodded to Cathy.

'I'll give him something to make him sleep,' she promised. 'If there's a spare ambulance, I'll get one to take him home, or else a taxi. You get back and rest now—you look done in.'

Cathy nodded exhaustedly. She kissed the old man's cheek gently, and watched as the nurse guided him towards the office. The surgeon's verdict had been so final, had carried so little hope ... Now, more than ever, she felt the depth of her closeness to Fabian. She needed him so badly. And over the next weeks, he was going to need much, too. Feeling as though her heart would break, she walked slowly down the corridor towards the exit.

As she emerged on to the landing, a woman was hurrying up the stairs. It was Cerise Hunniford, her hair now toned to a dull magenta red, and wearing a chartreuse green evening gown. At the sight of Cathy she stopped, her mascaraed eyes widening.

'Is he dead?' she asked abruptly. Cathy shook her head, unable to keep back her wince of pain at the way Cerise's question had clawed at her raw nerves.

'No. But he's badly hurt.' She drew a deep breath, not wanting to let her dislike for Cerise come between them now. 'The doctor says he may be blind— permanently.'

'Blind?' Cerise's face twisted in disgust. 'Oh, God! Is he scarred?'

'Not on his face.' Cathy shrugged. 'His head's bandaged, of course.' She studied the other woman tiredly, deciding from her glamorous turn-out, and the faint smell of alcohol that wafted from her with her perfume, that Cerise had been called from a party. 'They've just put him to sleep.'

'I see.' Cerise looked Cathy's unexceptional workwear up and down. 'I take it you've been at his bedside all night.'

'He's been in the operating theatre for over four hours,' Cathy said grimly. 'I've been waiting with Keith—Fabian's father.'

'I know who Keith Blackthorne is.' Cerise leaned back against the metal banister and lit a slim cigarillo, exhaling the smoke upwards. 'Blind,' she repeated, shaking her head. 'Are they sure?'

'The surgeon didn't hold out much hope,' Cathy said. The memory of Fabian's cold lips crossed her mind again, bringing the tears close to the surface again.

'Poor bastard. Poor, poor bastard.' Cerise met Cathy's eyes with a hard challenge. 'You don't look very perturbed about your beloved, *Miss* Milner.'

'He's not my beloved,' said Cathy, too tired and full of grief to respond to the taunt. 'And I've shed all my tears.'

'Oh, come on!' Cerise drew on her cigarillo again, her eyes narrowed. Cathy realised that she was more than a little drunk. 'You've had your knickers in a twist over Fabian Blackthorne for weeks. Why bother to deny it? I found the whole thing quite a joke. The fair virgin who had to be rescued by the lawyer on the white horse!' She snorted smoke out at Cathy.

'I'm tired, Cerise,' Cathy said unemotionally. 'And this doesn't seem to me a suitable occasion to exchange insults. Fabian may have lost his sight—for ever.'

'And I suppose you're shaping up to be Fabian's nursemaid?' jeered Cerise with a bitter smile. 'I bet you'd really fancy that—running around after a blind man, spooning his gruel into his mouth, telling him about the pretty flowers——'

'Stop!' Nauseous at the deliberate cruelty, Cathy pushed her way past Cerise. 'You make me sick,' she said in a shaky voice. 'I'm going home.'

Cerise's hand clamped around her arm, stopping her. 'You were all set to take him away from me, weren't you?' she said viciously. 'I was on the brink of deciding I had to do something about you, Miss Milner of Northwood. Why the hell *should* you have him? Just because you're ten years younger than me? You make me sick—with your privilege and your pearls!'

'I don't have any pearls,' Cathy said inconsequentially, feeling that this was a crazy, bad dream—scuffling with Cerise while Fabian lay blind upstairs.

'Well, *I* had him first,' Cerise said shrilly. 'And I wasn't going to give up to a green-eyed bitch like you——'

Cathy jerked her arm away, stopped from delivering a resounding slap to Cerise's flushed face only by the thought of the man upstairs.

'You're behaving like a fool,' she said tersely.

'Maybe I am.' Cerise's bright blue eyes became dim, and she shook her head. 'It's all over, anyway. All over.'

'He's not dead,' Cathy snapped.

'He might as well be,' Cerise retorted. 'There isn't a contest any more.' She waved her cigarillo in a clumsy gesture, her bright, thin mouth twisted. 'I can't stand disabilities. That's my weakness. Know that?' She met Cathy's eyes, her face contorted. 'I'm no good at looking after the world's lame ducks. I've had all that. I've had the whole bloody thing—up to here.' Cathy watched with dark, puzzled eyes as Cerise tossed her cigarillo down the stairwell.

'I don't know what you're talking about.'

'Why should you?' Cerise flickered a compact out of her handbag, and retouched her lipstick in the mirror. To her surprise, Cathy saw that there were now tears on the clotted eyelashes. 'It's none of your damned business, anyway.' She snapped the compact shut. 'I've got a present for you, little Miss Milner. You can have him, now. I don't want him any more.' With a savage smile, Cerise turned around, and clattered back down the stairs. 'I must get back to my party,' she said over her shoulder. 'I wish you joy of him.'

Cathy watched the acrid-green back disappear down the stairs. The anger drained slowly out of her. Cerise's pain was genuine. In her way, she was obviously fond of Fabian, and lashing out at Cathy had been her twisted way of showing it.

She followed slowly, grief and weariness leaving her numbed. A few weeks ago, she had been wallowing in self-pity over her idiotic behaviour with *Caprice*. How terrible her plight had seemed then, how maudlin she'd been about her misery. Fool, she cursed herself. From the perspective of this dreadful night, all that ballyhoo about the photographs had been a piffling adventure, the stupid mistake of a spoiled girl. She had suddenly seen what real suffering meant, what life could really do to people. How lucky she had been then, how very lucky!

And her break-up with Tim—that had seemed such a huge issue, dominating her thoughts and emotions. Unbelievable. It all seemed so shallow now, so lacking in depth. Compared to what had happened to Fabian, nothing in her life had been so bad after all.

Cathy huddled into her coat as the night air met her. She had been cold all day, as cold as ice. As though some vital warmth had left her body for ever.

She had lied to Cerise. She hadn't shed all her tears yet.

Not by a long way.

When Keith Blackthorne phoned her on Wednesday morning, almost exactly seven weeks after the accident, Cathy had a premonition of what was to come. In fact, she had been expecting it for some time now, expecting it with a feeling of dread.

'Will you meet me for lunch today, Cathy? I need to talk.'

'Of course,' she agreed.

'One o'clock at Scalabrino's? That's just along from your shop.'

'Of course,' she said again. 'How's Fabian this week?'

'Oh, he's doing fine. *Very* well.'

The false cheerfulness in his voice made Cathy wince as she put down the phone and turned back to the new consignment of carpets that had just arrived from Turkey.

He was waiting for her at a corner table, a frail-looking old man with introspective eyes. The Italian restaurant was crowded and noisy, packed with lunching business people, and they had to lean across over the checked tablecloth to hear each others' voices.

'How about a bottle of Chianti?'

'If you'll drink three-quarters of it,' she smiled. He wasn't looking well, she reflected, and his hair seemed to be turning from grey to white almost weekly. Over the pizza margharita he kept up the jolly façade, but the strain was so obvious in his lined face that Cathy reached out for his hand.

'You don't have to pretend with me, Keith. What is it?'

Tiredness eased the smile right off his face, and he pushed his plate away.

'I'm at my wits' end,' he said simply. 'Fabian's due to leave the centre next week, and there's literally nowhere he can go. They've convinced me that I wouldn't be much use looking after him.' He poured more of the blood-red wine into their glasses, oblivious to the splashes on the gaily checked cloth. 'He refuses to countenance the idea of more rehabilitation—says he's had enough. I don't blame him, Cathy; he's done magnificently since the accident. Yet I know that he'll never accept his blindness—not where it counts, inside. And he's a strong-willed man, you know that. I've never been able to force him into anything. I couldn't start doing so now.'

'I understand,' Cathy had said gently. 'And you know if there's anything I can do to help, I'll be only too glad.'

'Would you?' Keith's grey eyes were troubled as they searched her face. 'Cathy——' he began hesitantly, 'there's something I wanted to discuss with you. It's not actually my idea—Baker came up with it yesterday.'

'Go ahead,' she said, knowing what he was going to ask.

'The idea really grew out of the fact that you're about the only person Fabian responds to right now——'

'He only responds *sometimes*,' she corrected him. She drank the rough, somehow satisfying wine, and smiled. 'He's more likely than not to snap my head off, Keith.'

'But at least he trusts you.' An eager light had crept into the old man's eyes. 'And you're the only person who's been able to make him smile. Even I can't do that. Besides, you looked after your father after his coronary, didn't you? You know something about nursing—and you wouldn't have to give up your job——'

'Keith,' Cathy said quietly, 'what are you suggesting?'

'That you take him on, just for the first week or so,' Keith pleaded. 'Maybe even less. You're so calm, such a tranquil person. Maybe your calm would rub off on Fabian, make it easier for him——'

'Keith——' She opened her mouth, but ended by shrugging helplessly, not knowing what to say.

'Would it be too much?'

She stared into the grief-stricken eyes, her heart sinking rapidly. 'It's not that it would be too much. I just don't know whether I could do Fabian any good. I might even do him harm.' His expression cut her to the heart. How could she refuse? How could she?

'I took the liberty of speaking to your father about it this morning,' Keith went on. 'He agreed with me that you could only do Fabian good, Cathy. It's up to you to make your own mind up, of course,' he said seriously, 'and I don't want to pressurise you. But you see, the first week out of the rehabilitation centre is going to be crucial. It may determine how the rest of his life is going to go. Fabian doesn't have a mother—and I wouldn't trust any of his friends. But you—you're different.'

'Am I?' She slumped back in the chair. God, what a decision! Having sensed for days that it was coming somehow hadn't made the moment of decision any easier. She cared enough about Fabian, and was enough of a woman, to ache to help him, look after him. But she was no fool, either, and she had a good idea of exactly how horribly difficult looking after Fabian Blackthorne in his present mood would be. Would she be able to cope? 'I'm not a professional,' she sighed, almost to herself.

'No,' Keith Blackthorne said urgently. 'You're more. You've got something deeper than professionalism, a kind of love in you, that people respond to instinctively. Your father tells me you work at the Addington regularly? Well, that's exactly what I mean. You have that kind of personality, that kind of peace.'

'Keith, I'd like nothing more than to help Fabian. You've probably guessed that even before the accident I was——' She hesitated in embarassment. 'I like him very much. But——'

'Cathy,' he reached out for one of her hands, his eyes dark and grave, 'I know what I'm asking, child. I know just how difficult this would be—for both of you. Nor do I ask such a thing lightly. No other person in the world would I ask—except one. Fabian's mother. And she died twenty-six years ago.'

'I know that,' Cathy said wryly. 'Keith, if I'm to give any decision at all, it'll have to be on a trial period. One week. And if it doesn't work out—for Fabian, I mean— then we're going to have to find some other solution.'

She touched his hand. 'I care deeply about Fabian. I'm just afraid of failing him.'

'We're all afraid. And in our fear and ignorance, we all have to help one another in this life. And as for your personal feelings for Fabian——' he smiled tiredly, 'whatever is between you, it will only help. I'd like to be able to tell you that Fabian cares for you as much as you obviously care for him. I can't. I would guess that he does—but I can't guarantee that. But your love for him, Cathy——' She flinched at the word, and he nodded quietly. 'Your love for him may just save him. Think about it. Don't say anything now, just think about it.'

'I will,' she promised, as they rose to leave.

But she hadn't needed to think about it to know that she was going to agree.

Time had flown past since that dreadful night at the hospital, she thought wryly. The first week after the accident had been the greyest period her life had ever known. The days had seeped into one another in a kind of mental fog. She had never been so depressed, or felt so embittered against life. The daily visits to the hospital became an ordeal that she dreaded, an assault on her self-control that strained her to the utmost.

The doctors had kept Fabian dulled with drugs for the first few days, until the realisation that he was blind finally settled in, but there wasn't much they could do after that. The operation had left a clean scar about an inch long across his left temple, and as soon as the dark hair began to grow again, it was all but covered. Apart from that, the accident had left him with nothing worse than contusions.

Physically, that was.

His mental response was far more complex, and coping with it had made huge demands on Cathy. His courage was phenomenal—but beneath it lay a smouldering anger that was almost tangible, like the heat from a banked-down furnace. Cathy found his bravery almost frightening. In a sense, she would have preferred him to explode, to release his pain and horror in a period of rage. That was what she personally would have done. And had Fabian done so, she might have been able to share his release, to purge herself of some of her own fear and anger against life.

But he didn't. He remained grim-faced and quietly savage, his strong fingers clenching involuntarily against the inner emotions he was dealing with.

And no one seemed able to get through that wall of steel. Not Cathy, nor Keith Blackthorne, still himself shaken and despairing in the wake of what had happened to his son. Not the friends and colleagues who came to his bedside to share the awkward silences with Cathy, and left in relief when visiting time was over.

He had liked to listen to her talk, contributing only monosyllabic comments to the conversation, and on one afternoon he let her hold his hand in a—for her—shaky silence. But what his real feelings were, she could only guess. As for any emotional relationship between them—that seemed to have frozen into nothingness.

'It's not an uncommon reaction,' Mr Baker had told Cathy privately when she had asked about it. 'He's going through hell right now, and there's very little we can do to help him. I'm ashamed to admit it, but we simply aren't equipped to do more than attend to his physical damage—and we've done our best.' He had sighed wearily. 'He's due to be discharged soon, as you know. I've recommended that he go to the Sark Institute—it's a rehabilitation centre for the blind where he'll be able to learn some basic skills. It's up to him whether he goes or not, but he won't get very far without that kind of help.' The surgeon paused. 'My advice would be to find help of another kind, as well.'

'You mean psychiatric help?'

'If that becomes necessary. Even after he's been helped by the people at the Institute, he'll need all the support he can get, Miss Milner. He's frightened and angry, and he's going to stay that way for a long time. Be warned that he's apt to lash out at anyone who tries to help. But for his own good, he's going to need someone to look after him while he adjusts to——'

To eternal night. To the rest of his life in darkness.
Cathy shuddered at the thought of what he must be
going through, her heart yearning out to him.

Fabian had gone to the Sark Institute. Cathy had
kept up her visits, at least twice a week when she could
manage it. Like Fabian himself, she had forced herself
to put her emotional feelings for him into a kind of
deep-freeze; they'd only get in the way right now. If
they survived the thaw that might come, years from
now, if . . .

But Mr Baker's conversation with Cathy had been
the start of a decision-making process that had led up
to Keith Blackthorne's approach this morning. Looking
back now, she knew that there was little she could have
done, or had wanted to do, to avoid the responsibility
that was now being offered to her.

Mr Baker had repeated what he had told her to Keith
Blackthorne—and though he was pathetically eager to
care for his son, it was obvious to everyone that he was
simply incapable. For one thing, he was too upset after
the accident. For another, like Cedric Milner, he was an
ageing man living on his own. Fabian's mother had
died when Fabian was a boy, and Keith Blackthorne
had never been the homely type anyhow.

Making the decision, then, was a strangely undram-
atic business. Cathy went back to work from the
restaurant, her green eyes clouded with thought; and by
the time she was driving home, her mind had been
made up. She couldn't refuse to help Fabian.

Persuading Fabian to accept help was a different
matter.

Wisely, she had left that to his father. She guessed
that Fabian wouldn't take kindly to the idea of being
cared for by Cathy Milner, and she deliberately stayed
away from the centre for several days while Keith
Blackthorne tried to explain to his son that Cathy was
to look after him from now on.

And when Keith came to her to tell her that Fabian
had agreed to the idea, his face was sombre.

'He isn't exactly overjoyed,' he had warned. 'I'm so sorry, Cathy. My son's an ungrateful devil sometimes——'

'I think I know how he feels,' she said with a wry smile.

'But at least he's accepted that it's the only way. And a word of warning——'

'Yes?'

'If a father's opinion means anything, I'd guess that Fabian cares a lot about you. And that means he respects your opinion. He feels that his blindness has somehow made him—I don't know. It sounds crazy, but he feels himself to be less than a man now.'

'I know,' she whispered, closing her eyes. 'I can understand it—but it's so crazy.'

'Yes,' Keith said dully. 'But there it is. And what I'm trying to tell you is that he'll be extra-sensitive with you, maybe even cruel. I wish there was something I could say to him—but on top of his suffering, a father's nagging would be useless. There's something else, too.'

'What is it?'

'The most important thing you could do for Fabian, Cathy, is make him accept his blindness.' He looked into her eyes. 'Make him accept that it's permanent and irrevocable. He won't thank you for doing that——' Cathy grimaced, feeling her heart sink, '—but once he's over that barrier, I feel he has a real chance for happiness.'

That was an unbelievably tall order, she thought, but didn't say the words. And it was with a sense of foreboding, a few days later, that she arrived at the rehabilitation centre to take Fabian home. He was waiting for her in the discharge office—and when she met his piercing grey eyes, her stomach jolted with the irrational idea he could see her. She always felt that. Insane as it seemed, those diamond-bright eyes could see nothing. Almost afraid of him, she halted in front of his chair.

'Fabian?'

'Ah,' he said grimly. 'My little nursemaid.' He rose to

his feet, questing for her. The weeks since the accident had taken ten pounds off his powerful frame, and his face was fierce, the bronzed skin taut over the bone. Sensing her timid appraisal, his mouth tightened. 'What's the matter? Do I look any different?'

'You look fine,' she said stupidly.

'Thank you.' His politeness was abrasive, meant to wound. 'Now tell me how *you* look.'

'I—your father's sent some of your clothes and things over to Northwood. I've got your room ready. It's all waiting for you there.'

'Wonderful!'

'My car's just outside.'

'Clever you!'

In dismay, Cathy glanced at the senior staff nurse, who looked studiously bland.

'Goodbye, Mr Blackthorne,' she said with professional jollity. 'I'm sure you're in good hands now. You know we're always here if you need us.'

'Shall we go?' Cathy suggested hastily, anticipating some poisonous retort from Fabian.

'Yes, let's go, for God's sake. Anything will be better than this place.' Suddenly he reached out a hand, and brushed her face with probing fingers. She flinched, then held still as he traced the contours of her eyelids, her mouth, her slender throat.

'It *is* me,' she said drily, trying to disguise the way his touch had set her heart fluttering. His fingers slid through her dark hair, sending shivers down her spine.

'You've had your hair cut.'

'It was far too long.' She hesitated. 'You must have a good memory.'

'I'll adapt,' Fabian said sardonically. 'The world is full of blind lawyers.' He shrugged at her awkward silence. 'Let's go.'

He strode towards the door, his movements making no concession to the fear and uncertainty he must be feeling. But the door was half closed, and she called out too late; Fabian slammed into the edge of the door, his cheek cannoning off the wood with a sickening crack.

'Oh God!' she groaned softly, taking his arm. 'Are you all right?'

'Leave me be!' he snapped, white with fury. He shook her arm off with savage strength.

'I'm sorry,' she said helplessly.

'I don't want your damned sorrow,' he snarled. 'Remember that, Cathy. Not now. Not ever!'

Gritting her teeth, she reached for his arm again. 'Don't be a fool, Fabian. Your life has changed. Outside the walls of this place there'll be nobody to stop you from walking into things. And you can't bulldoze your way through every obstacle. Now let me show you the way.'

Silent, his face tense, he clamped steel fingers around her upper arm. Suppressing pain and anger, she led him down to the car.

His stormy grey eyes were fixed on nothing, yet from time to time they flickered, as though he were watching scenes within his mind. Cathy had noticed that before. It was symbolic of how he was, she thought, locked into his own world of pain and anger. Was anything ever going to get him out?

He was silent during the long drive out to Northwood. From time to time she glanced at him, trying to assess his state of mind. He was physically as stunning as ever; yet every time she cornered or braked, his face would tighten, and his hands would brace against the dashboard.

'Is my driving that bad?' she asked sarcastically.

'I can't tell,' he said quietly. 'I don't have very happy memories of my last experience in a car.'

Biting her lip, Cathy cursed her own thoughtlessness, and slowed down to half-speed. They relapsed into a grim silence that lasted until the gravel drive crunched under the car's wheels.

'We're here,' she said, trying to sound gay. 'Dad'll be waiting for us inside.' But Fabian made no effort to move. Instead, he leaned back in his seat, closing his eyes, and sighed.

'It's good to hear birds singing again.' His voice was

husky, gentler than she had heard it since the accident. 'Funny how important sounds become.' He turned to her, a slow smile wryly curving his lips. 'Things have changed, haven't they, Cathy?'

'You're still the same man, Fabian,' she said uncertainly. It was hard not to imagine that those splendid grey eyes weren't looking directly into her soul. 'I mean—you're the same inside.'

'Am I?' The smile tightened. 'Don't let's kid ourselves. Why did you agree to take me, Cathy?'

'I—I wanted to help——'

'Did you have glamorous expectations of what caring for a blind man was going to be like? Or are you just the sentimental type?'

'There's no sentiment involved,' she said, recoiling from the acid in his voice. 'I told you—I just wanted to help. You helped me when I was in trouble.'

'Yeah. What have you got planned for me? Cuddly toys and taped books?' His big hands gripped the dashboard with bitter strength. 'Or are you planning to offer me the comforts of your beautiful body?'

'I haven't planned anything, as a matter of fact,' she gritted.

'No?' The hard mockery on his face deepened. 'Not even alms for the blind man?' His fingers knotted painfully in her hair, pulling her face to his so that she could feel his breath hot against her lips. 'How far does your devotion extend, Cathy? Or is your so-called pity some kind of kinky turn-on?' He kissed her, hard and cruelly, then released her, leaving her with bruised lips and an aching heart. 'Don't ever offer me pity, Cathy. Never. Now, let's go and see your father.'

The evening was difficult. Keith Blackthorne arrived after dinner, looking worn and old, and insisted that Cathy and her father remain with him and Fabian. But the elderly lawyer was still obviously too shaken by the catastrophe to show anything more than a glimmering of sociability. And Fabian, his blind eyes grim and his jaw-muscles knotted, was savagely indifferent to all that went on. Cathy alone struggled to keep the conversation buoyant, to little avail. By nine o'clock Keith Blackthorne had gone, and Sir Cedric Milner excused himself with ill-disguised relief, and went to bed, leaving Cathy and Fabian alone.

Alone in the room where, bare weeks before, Fabian had made her pulses surge, her mind and body thrill to his touch. It felt like something that had happened years ago, a lifetime ago.

As she poured coffee into his cup, she glanced at the set, bronzed face, still staring with those iron-grey eyes into infinity. He hadn't smiled, she realised, since the accident. Those narrow lips, capable of so much passion, were set in a taut line. He moved his head slightly, thick dark lashes lowering over his eyes.

'Are you looking at me?'

'Yes,' she said, flushing. 'How did you know?'

'There was a pitying hush,' he said drily. 'You've all been tiptoeing around me tonight as though I were a delicate baby that mustn't be wakened.'

'Have we?' Cathy put his coffee-cup into his hands, anger building up inside her. 'Doesn't it occur to you that other people might have feelings too? Your father, for example. This has hit him very badly. He looks old, shaken. No one particularly feels like singing and dancing, Fabian.'

'I'm sorry to be such a depression on you all,' he said acidly. 'But if you knew I was going to spoil your party, why the hell did you bring me here?'

'Because——' She bit her lip. She desperately wanted to tell him how horrified she was by what had happened to him, but she knew that he would explode if he thought she pitied him. And his abrasive manner wasn't making things any easier. 'Because I thought we were friends,' she said in a low voice. 'You got me off the hook when I'd been such a fool about those pictures. That meant a lot to me, Fabian.' She searched his dark face, looking in vain for any sign of softening. 'I want to help, that's all.'

'Okay,' Fabian shrugged, 'so you want to help. You

won't help by clucking over me as though I were a little boy with a sore finger.'

She bit back the retort that was on her tongue.

'Very well, what do you want me to do, then?'

'Why do you have to *do* anything?' he asked with impatient sarcasm. 'You keep talking as though the Third World War had broken out, and tomorrow was Doomsday. It's not like that.'

'Being blind isn't exactly a minor complaint,' she snapped without thinking.

'I know,' he said drily, and blood rushed to her cheeks at her stupidity. 'Look,' he went on, 'I'm not deformed, Cathy. There's nothing wrong with my mind or my body. I'm not going to die next week, or even next year. I'm not in any pain.' His face tightened imperceptibly. 'Not in any physical pain. And just because I happen to have lost my sight it doesn't mean I'm going to spend the rest of my life crawling around on all fours blubbering over my fate.'

Silenced by this glimpse of his inner feelings, she could only watch the handsome, dark face, trying desperately to understand.

'I'm not going to pretend that nothing's changed.' He shrugged. 'Life's become a lot harder for me. And that means that I have to make a corresponding effort. I'm a fighter, Cathy. I always have been.' She nodded silently. 'And what's more, I'm a winner.' He rose with that pantherine grace she knew so well, and made his way unerringly to the french doors, where once before he had held her in his arms, listening quietly as she wrenched out the secrets of her life. 'I have to learn how to deal with what's happened to me. Because I want my life. I want my career. And nothing's going to stop me—nothing!' He turned to face her, his passionate mouth set with grim authority. 'That means learning new skills, improving old ones. Not just vegetating. And never giving in to self-pity. Never.' He turned, and stared out into the garden, as though he could see the sprinkling of stars in the ultramarine sky. 'Come here,' he commanded softly. She went to join him, knowing that he could sense the warmth of her body beside him. 'Listen to me, girl. I realise that you're bursting with sympathy, but I don't want it. It doesn't help me to do what I have to do. It——' he struggled to find the words, 'it holds me back. Makes me weaker, not stronger. Can you understand that?'

'I think so——' she hesitated, trying desperately to take in what he was telling her. How much braver than her he was, she thought helplessly, with so much more strength. And how far out of her reach. She longed to touch him, with a longing that seemed to strain at her whole being. As if sensing her inner struggle, Fabian smiled softly to himself.

'Besides, blindness is only a matter of degree.'

'I don't understand.' She looked up into the face she cared so much for, and yet was so afraid of.

'When you lose your sight, you realise that the human senses aren't separate. They're a barrage of information and impulses that's somehow continuous. Taste isn't distinct. Sighted people don't sift through a quarter of the information their bodies give them.'

'For example?' she puzzled.

'For example—I have a picture of you right now. Call it a vision. You tell me if I'm wrong.' He leaned against the doorway, his face thoughtful. 'Okay. You've given up smoking.'

'Yes,' she said in surprise.

'No smell of nicotine, no sound of matches—easy. Let's go on. Tonight you're wearing a cotton dress. I'd guess it comes down to your knees. And I'd guess it's a pale floral print.' He smiled at her gasp of surprise. 'Easy again. I happen to know your taste. And the sound that cotton makes is quite different from, say, silk or nylon. You're wearing sandals—quite a short heel. I can tell by the click when you walk. And no stockings.' His grin was wicked. 'The sound of nyloned legs is totally distinct from the sound of bare legs. When you walk, I can hear the sound of your thighs brushing together, Cathy. When you crossed your legs just now, it was equivalent to a colour transparency in my mind.' She was blushing furiously, and he chuckled deep in his chest. 'I can feel the heat radiating off you. Why? It happens to be a very erotic sound. You've got such smooth, silky skin. And such good legs.'

'You can't tell that,' she snapped.

'No,' he admitted, 'but I have a good memory. There's a little silvery scar on your right knee. Am I right?'

'Yes,' she muttered, not knowing whether to be angry, amazed, or thrilled.

'Right—let me go on. You washed your hair the day before yesterday. I smelled the shampoo on your hair. It's still there today, though fainter. I'd guess some kind of rosemary extract.' He leaned towards her, inhaling the scent of her hair. 'Rosemary and thyme. Right again?'

'Yes,' she gulped.

'And that perfume you're wearing. Something by Guerlain. I don't quite remember the name—is it *Chamade*?'

'How in heaven did you know that?' she gaped.

'It isn't a very new bottle. Probably over a year old.'

'You're joking!'

'Not at all,' he said gravely. 'It's gone ever so slightly off. Not unpleasant—just a little fainter and muskier. Quite sexy, really.'

'I didn't realise you were such an expert on perfume,' she said acidly. 'Years of female companions, no doubt?'

'Anyone who loves beautiful women has to love beautiful perfume,' he smiled. 'Now here's an easy one—a new leather handbag.'

'Driving gloves, actually,' she retorted, meanly glad to have proved him wrong in his amazing catalogue. 'But not bad.' He nodded indifferently, and went on.

'Tonight you have very little make-up on. No lipstick. Nothing except a little mascara and maybe a brushing of eye-shadow—dark blue to set off your eyes. That's easier than you think,' he smiled drily as she watched in amazement. 'Make-up—most of it—smells really horrible. Even lipstick. And it tastes worse.' A reminiscent smile curved briefly over his mouth. 'Okay, from here on we move into the realms of guesswork. It's a warm night. So you're not wearing a cardigan or shawl. Your dress leaves your arms bare. You've got good arms, so I guess you like to show them off. Short nails—I don't hear any clicks when you touch material—and no bangles clattering your wrists. I think I remember a thin gold ring, though.'

'A sixteenth birthday present from my mother.' Cathy was incredibly uncomfortable at this exploration of her body, no matter how remote. It was somehow so intimate, so shockingly accurate. It jolted her to realise how closely his mind had been following her. 'Go on,' she invited in wry perplexity.

'Not much more to tell. You didn't eat much at dinner. You had water while the rest of us had wine. I can't smell anything on your breath. Oh—except the chocolates you sneaked while I was talking to my father.' He shrugged. 'You don't have to be Sherlock Holmes to work these things out, Cathy. I'm just telling you all this to try and show you that although I'm blind, I still see things. I don't need your pity.'

'Point taken,' she said quietly. Fabian's face became sombre.

'I'm afraid, Cathy. Sometimes the blackness seems to hem me in, to crush me, obliterate me, all I am, all the things I want to be. I want to scream for someone to put on the light. It's a kind of mental claustrophobia, and it makes me panic.'

'You never show it,' she whispered.

'I can't afford to. There's nowhere for me to run. I have to fight it—fight it and win. Otherwise I'd just go mad, period.'

She reached out timidly to touch him, but he shook her hand off disdainfully.

'Paws off,' he said sharply. 'What have I just been telling you?' His face was closed now. To her dismay, she realised that this rare, privileged insight into his mind was now over. The audience is terminated. Now get out.

'I understand,' she said hastily, though she didn't.

'I doubt it. But if you think about it long enough, even you might be able to work it out.' Coldly, he turned on his heel, and walked back into the drawing-room.

Cathy followed, taken aback by the quickness of his moods.

'I'm going to bed,' he said shortly. 'Sorry to have bored you.'

'I wasn't bored,' she told him urgently. 'I was——'

'Goodnight, Cathy.' He stalked towards the door, while she watched him in near-tearful surprise.

'I don't understand you,' she whispered. His sharp ears caught the words, and when he turned to face her, his smile was cruel, mocking.

'Then thank God you don't have to do an exam on me. Because you'd fail every time, Cathy.'

'But I'm trying my hardest,' she pleaded. 'I want to give you so much——'

'Keep your gifts. If they were sincere, they might mean something.'

And leaving her dumbstruck, he walked deliberately through the door, and into the darkness of the unlighted hallway. The darkness to which he was as indifferent as to the brightest light.

CHAPTER SEVEN

OVER the next few days, Cathy began to believe that their conversation of that evening, difficult and explosive as it had been, represented a minor breakthrough. For the first time, at least, Fabian had talked to her about his inner feelings. He had admitted to her the frustrations and tensions—and above all, the fear—which he faced every second of every day.

His aggression towards her wasn't a personal thing, she was sure of that. Rather, it was a kind of lightning flash that had no choice but to explode. She had agreed to try and care for Fabian, no matter how great the difficulties. Well, now was the time for her to face those difficulties.

And Fabian was working with grim determination. With a cassette tape-recorder which the people at the Institute had shown him how to use, he was battling to find a way of dealing with his legal work. He was also continuing the Braille course which he had begun at the Institute, something which was obviously causing him severe headaches and frustrations. It made Cathy ache sometimes to see the way he hurled himself, body and soul, against the locked door of his blindness. As to his career, she couldn't help feeling that it would be many months before he was adept enough to be able to practise fully again. The urge to work seemed to drive him relentlessly on, though, as though he couldn't bear the feeling of being idle, of rusting away. Where many a man would have slumped into bitter accept- ance, Fabian fought with a singleminded determina- tion that Cathy began to think might even work miracles.

In fact, despite her resolution otherwise, it was increasingly difficult for her to control her own feelings about Fabian. She knew that they were deepening steadily, becoming more serious. But where they were leading, she couldn't say. The more she understood him, the more she loved his courage, his determination, the flashes of wry humour which nothing seemed able to suppress; but she was still afraid of him, so conscious of his power to wound, or his power to seduce her physically, that she almost wanted to run away from him.

One sunny afternoon, she felt she had enough confidence to take Fabian riding. She hired horses at the riding school near by, and led him across the meadows towards the trees. The woods were delicious, cool and bird-filled.

'I came here the week after we went to see the *Caprice* people,' she told him, 'and thought about you. I didn't imagine you'd be tangling yourself in Cerise Hunniford's web, of course.' She shot him a jealous little glance. 'Or was it the other way round?'

He sat ramrod-straight on the horse, in this as in all other things, deliberately making no concession to uncertainty or fear. The bleak grey eyes stared out ahead, not seeing her moods.

'Cerise?' he shrugged. 'She's an intelligent woman. I liked her, not much more.'

'Oh?' Cathy walked her horse closer to his. 'She gave me the impression that her feelings were rather stronger.'

He turned to her, one eyebrow arching. 'And when did you last see Cerise?'

'I——' She bit her lip. 'At the hospital, the night of your accident. She was coming to see you.'

'I don't remember Cerise being there,' he said, frowning.

'You were asleep then.' Cathy fiddled with her reins. 'Besides, she didn't come into your room. We just met in the corridor and talked.'

'What about?'

'You.' She remembered Cerise's eyes, sharp with dislike, and the smell of brandy on her breath. Fabian must have been bitterly hurt by the fact that Cerise hadn't ever come to see him since the accident, but he hadn't shown it. As if reading her thoughts, Fabian shrugged.

'Unlike you, it seems Cerise Hunniford isn't an angel of mercy.' His horse stumbled slightly, and he steadied himself against the animal's neck. 'You don't happen to know why she hasn't put in an appearance, do you?'

She searched Fabian's face, longing to know his true feelings about Cerise. Should she repeat Cerise's cold words? Perhaps it would best to be brutally frank, get it over with. Hesitantly, she went on, 'She gave me the impression that she'd rather not see you now that you're blind. To use your phrase, she gave me the impression that she wasn't much good in the angel of mercy role.'

'I see.' Muscles bunched in his jaw, and with dismay she noticed that his face was pale. So he *did* care about Cerise—a great deal! Unhappily, Cathy tried to explain further.

'She told me that she'd had—I don't know, some kind of experience, something in her past which haunted her still. That seeing you now would only upset her. I didn't understand what she was saying—you know I'm not exactly her favourite person.'

'I suppose not,' he said in a leaden voice. Aching, she glanced at him. It hadn't been exactly tactful to repeat Cerise's harsh sentences, and she bitterly regretted having done so now.

'Are you—are you very disappointed?' she asked softly.

'Disappointed?' With an effort, he seemed to come to himself. 'Not really.' He gave a harsh laugh, the pain in his face made more visible, rather than less so, in doing so.

'At least she's honest. She doesn't waste time on false sympathy. Unlike you.'

'Meaning what?' asked Cathy in a quiet voice. 'I don't understand you, Fabian.'

'Don't you?' he asked indifferently.

'No!' Frustration and pain were making her lose her

self-control now. 'You talk as if you actually admired Cerise for abandoning you, and as though you despised me for trying to show that I care! Why?'

'I don't despise you for that,' he said more gently. 'I doubt whether any other human being could have handled me the way you've done over these past few weeks.'

'Then what is it?' she demanded, too upset to feel any pleasure at his words. 'Why are you always so antagonistic towards me? Why did you want me to look after you if you hated me so much?'

'I don't hate you.' His calmness was galling. 'You're shallow and childish sometimes, yes. But I don't hate you.'

Shallow and childish? More hurt than she cared to admit, even to herself, Cathy said, 'I see. Well, that's a relief.'

'You sound annoyed,' he said ironically. 'Am I unfair?'

'Just a little,' she retorted. 'You're not very grateful.'

'Oh, so you're in this for the gratitude?'

'You know I'm not,' she snapped. 'But I'd do anything for you Fabian, anything at all. You know that. And it's not very just of you to throw that in my face.' Tears were trembling just behind her words. 'I realise that you're deeply unhappy, that you're struggling to keep yourself going—but that doesn't give you the right to trample all over my feelings!'

'And *my* feelings?' Fabian's face was angry. 'Do you really imagine that I'm indifferent to you, Cathy?'

'You are,' she accused. 'You don't give a damn!'

'You're wrong,' he said quietly, his mouth still tense. 'It doesn't occur to you that my hostility towards you is only self-defence?'

'Self-defence?' Cathy shook her head in scorn. 'That's crazy! There's nothing you have to defend yourself from. I couldn't possibly hurt you, not in a million years.'

'That's what you think,' he said shortly. 'I get tired of being just a game to you, Cathy.'

'You're *not* a game to me,' she snapped furiously. 'That's unworthy of you!'

'And you don't understand a thing,' he growled, his anger rising to meet hers. 'You're overloaded with sentimental little notions.'

'Maybe my little notions, as you call them, go a lot deeper than you imagine,' she said fiercely.

'What are you talking about?' he asked grimly. 'You don't mean tender romance and moonlight? Come on, Cathy!'

'I mean real feelings,' she said shakily. 'Emotions that you wouldn't even understand——'

'Or couldn't afford, even if I did understand them,' he broke in drily. 'Can't *you* understand that the very last thing I want right now is any emotional entanglement—especially not with you!'

'Why not? Because I'm shallow and childish?'

'Yes,' he retorted. He reached out with iron fingers and grasped her bridle, forcing her to a standstill. 'You just can't play around with my emotions, girl, not the way I am now. Use your brain, for God's sake!'

'But I just want to make things easier for you——'

'You can't.' His voice cut through her sentence like a whip. 'Not the way you're going now. You can neither understand nor help. You're too clumsy, too inexperienced. Too *young*.'

She stared through blurred eyes at his set face. Why does it all have to be so difficult, so confused? Why are you so far from me, my love? Why do you hurt me so, make me so angry? Aloud, she said in a low voice, 'Maybe it was a mistake your coming here, Fabian. We just don't seem to fit, do we?'

'Cathy, Cathy . . .' He shook his head in despair, his mouth pulled down in a bittersweet smile. 'You don't understand, do you?'

'I only understand that nothing I do is right.'

'No, that isn't true. Sometimes you're wonderful. I just can't take your emotionalism, that's all.'

'No, you'd rather have Cerise's version of honesty,' she snapped.

'Cerise again.' His brows descended ominously. 'Why always Cerise? What makes you so obsessed with her?'

'Can't you guess?' she said bitterly. 'Because you'd rather be with her than me. Except that Cerise isn't available, so you have to settle for second best.'

'Is that what you think?' he asked quietly.

'Well?' she challenged. 'Isn't it true?'

'The relationship I had with Cerise was uncomplicated, at least,' he replied coolly. 'Which is more than I can say for the relationship I have with you.'

'By "uncomplicated" I suppose you mean "sexual"?' she sneered.

'If that's what you want to think.'

'Cerise was your lover, wasn't she?' Cathy went on, not trying to hold back her jealousy and anger any more.

'If you like,' he replied in the same indifferent voice

'It's what *you* like that I'm after,' she said unevenly, ignoring the warning signs of anger at his lips and eyes. 'Nothing I do for you means a thing, does it? You'd rather have Cerise's *uncomplicated* body. Or would you rather have mine?' she went on bitterly.

'The idea had crossed my mind,' he said. His voice was still calm, but there was a tension in him that should have warned her. But Cathy was past all warnings. All the emotion she had bottled up over the past weeks, all the fear, the frustrated love she had been holding in, was now boiling over in a nervous outburst she was unable to control.

'Well, Cerise isn't the only one who can offer that kind of comfort,' she said with trembling defiance.

'Meaning?' he asked dangerously.

'Meaning that I'm available—if you want me.' She stared at him, the words quivering on the air. His stormy grey eyes were fixed intently on her face, almost as though they could pierce the darkness and see into her very soul. Then he swung his legs over the horse's back with easy grace, and slid to the ground.

'Very well,' he said calmly.

'Wh—what——'

'I accept your offer,' said Fabian. He came to her horse's side and reached up strong arms for her. She gasped as he drew her down with ruthless efficiency. 'Now,' he grunted, straightening her, 'you did mean what you said, didn't you?'

'Y-yes,' she said, in blank horror that he had taken her foolish bravado so seriously.

'Good,' he smiled quietly, and took her possessively in his arms, the contact with his hard body almost taking her breath away. Cathy looked up into his face, a fluttering of panic rising in her breast.

'You're trembling,' he said in a deep, soft voice. 'Like a dove in a trap. Do I frighten you, girl?'

'Now and then,' she admitted. She was still clinging to his arms, her fingers tasting the hard muscles there.

'Or is it disgust?' he queried with a dark smile. 'Being blind hasn't taken away any of my other capacities. Nor any of my desires.' His hands slid roughly down her flanks to her hips and pulled her forward against him, as he had done once before, so that she became acutely aware of his surging need against her body. 'You can tell that, can't you?' he asked, irony lifting one dark eyebrow.

'What—what do you want?' she asked, her voice dry in her throat, her heart pounding against her ribs.

'Just you.' His right hand slid up under her loose cotton shirt she wore, caressing her flinching skin on the way to cup her breast. The nipple strained out against him through the fine silk, and a profound weakness seemed to melt her from within. 'Your heart knows what I want,' he purred, his eyes intent on her with that uncanny impression of really being able to see her. 'I can feel it beating.'

'Fabian, don't do this to me——'

'Call it therapy,' he smiled mockingly. The horses were cropping the grass on the forest floor, unconcerned, and only the hum of the drowsy bees penetrated the summer hush. Cathy closed her eyes giddily as he kissed her temple, his breath warm in the dark cloud of her hair. He inhaled deeply.

'God, it's good to smell a woman again,' he sighed urgently. 'You've no idea how precious smells and sounds become in the darkness. And you smell of summer.' Hungrily, he buried his mouth in the soft curls next to her ear. 'Of summer and young grass. Of flowers and apples . . .'

'Fabian . . .' She could feel herself starting to melt as he unhooked her bra.

'My sweet Cathy . . .'

His hands were warm on the naked curves of her breasts, brushing the buds of her nipples, making her gasp. As her mind and body began dissolving into warm honey, it came to her in a revelation that much of his anger against her, the savage way he reacted towards her, stemmed from this—this blazing need for her, this desire he had been trying to hold in check. It was a love-hate, a bittersweet passion that rocked her to her emotional foundations.

Except that now hate was succumbing to love. All the bitterness that had passed was dissolving in the meltingpot of mutual passion. Convincing her that she loved this man, that her body was willing, oh, so willing to welcome his desire, to take Fabian's passion and return it—even though in some tiny logical room in her mind she knew that no tenderness accompanied his need.

Knew that to him she was a woman, no more—any woman. Any quivering body responding to the expert hunger of his lovemaking . . .

She did not resist as he lowered her on to the warm grass. Her passion was as taut as a bowstring, awaiting the release of his desire.

'I want you, Cathy,' he whispered, his voice husky. His fingers were ripping at the buttons of his shirt, impatient almost to desperation. The sun splashed in golden pools over and around them. Somewhere a meadowlark was singing, impossibly high and sweet. His body was magnificent, bronzed and satin-skinned. The dark, crisp hair on his chest and stomach made him almost primitive, and his maleness struck her like a blow.

'Fabian,' she said breathlessly. The gleaming power of his broad shoulders and sinewy arms was familiar from her dreams. Weak and shaking, she caressed the hot skin, thrilling to the pulse of the hard muscles beneath, her fingers brushing across his chest, the muscular column of his throat, caressing his cheek in a timid yet bold surrender. His mouth claimed hers, as all-encompassing as night.

His kiss was a thrusting dominion that took control of her, a demanding authority that she had no way of denying. His lips burst through her half-hearted defence, seeming to pierce her innermost heart. She clung to him, intoxicated by the touch of his naked skin against hers. The hair on his chest was ruthless against her nipples, his mouth plundering her mouth. Under her hands the muscles of his back were tight and hard.

He tore his mouth away from hers, his breath matching her own ragged gasps.

'Dear heaven, I wish I could see you,' he groaned. He had pulled open her shirt, and her full breasts were naked to the sun, their cream curves stark against his own bronzed muscularity. 'I remember your beauty,' he said huskily, tracing the shape of her throat with exquisitely sensitive fingers. 'I remember your green eyes, Cathy, your hair the colour of a raven's wing . . .'

'Darling,' she whispered, her love for him aching inside her like a fever, 'I can see you—and you're so beautiful, Fabian.' She could say no more. Her emotion was welling up inside her, a love too great for her to articulate. His clear grey eyes were smiling—blindness had not taken away their ability to do that—and the curve on his passionate mouth melted her senses.

His hands found her breasts again, and she arched helplessly against his caress, lost in the sheer power he exerted over her. It was wrong, though, she knew that somewhere inside the maelstrom.

Wrong because he didn't love her.

'Wait,' she pleaded, suddenly wanting to regain control. 'Fabian, please——'

'Silly girl,' he mocked gently, and leaned over her

nakedness to kiss where he had been caressing. 'Don't tell me you're getting scruples at this stage!' His mouth was a sweet torment that was cruelly designed to make her ache for more. In another few seconds, she knew, she would be unable to resist, would be his to take, here in this sunlit glade, under a blue summer sky.

'Don't,' she implored again, her voice heartbroken. 'Fabian, I can't take any more of this!'

'Then let's not wait,' he said in a savage growl that made her ache to the pit of her stomach. 'God, I need you, Cathy——' Her mouth was smothered by his as his fingers tugged roughly at her jeans. Desperately, she tried to resist, but he was strong, unbelievably strong. She was helpless in his arms, her will obliterated in the fierce sea of his desire.

'No,' she whimpered against the musky smell of his body, 'no—not like this——'

'There's no other way.' His kiss was rough, yet incredibly tender. 'You can't deny us this, Cathy. You can't!'

'Tell me you care about me, at least,' she begged, her eyes swimming like ameralds in her tears of anguish. 'Tell me you love me, tell me you care!'

Sudden anger blazed in his face. 'Let's not lie to each other, Cathy,' he growled. 'Why do you want deceptions?'

'I want the truth,' she cried, 'only the truth.'

'The truth is that I want you. And you want me. We don't need to know anything else.'

'You're wrong, Fabian,' she said in a low voice. 'There's more to it than that. There has to be.'

'You mean you don't want me?' he mocked, his eyebrows arching.

'Not like this. Not like this.'

'No?' She could not control herself as he reached out to touch her, possessive, utterly sure of himself. She gasped, all her strength melting. 'Your body says otherwise,' he murmured, his voice deep against her ear. She whimpered at the unbearable pleasure-pain of his touch, her nails digging involuntarily into the taut muscles of his arms.

'Your body is more honest than your mind, my sweet Cathy. There's no deception in it, no need for lies.'

'You are cruel,' she whispered helplessly. 'I trusted you. I trusted you.'

'And I've wanted you for too long. I've wanted you ever since you walked into my office that morning, Cathy. Ever since I saw the fear and pain in your eyes, and wanted to protect you. Can't you feel how much I need you?'

'What about afterwards?' she demanded bitterly. 'What will you feel afterwards? Anything? Nothing? Will I be just another conquest, another woman you devoured to ease your pain?'

'It isn't like that,' he said, his arms tight around her.

'Then how is it? Are you doing this to humiliate me? Because in your judgment I'm shallow and childish? Is this your idea of a punishment?'

'Don't be a fool,' he snapped.

'But I *am* a fool,' Cathy said in a trembling voice. His refusal to admit that he cared even a jot for her had made her feel utterly betrayed, hurt. 'You've made a fool of me, from first to last.' She drew away from him, tugging her shirt closed with unsteady fingers. 'I'm going back to the house, Fabian.'

He leaned back on one arm, the muscles of his shoulders and chest coming into magnificent relief. But his mouth was a hard line of anger, and his eyes were fierce slits.

'What is this?' he grated. 'Part of your little game?'

'There's no game,' she replied in a flat voice, her face pale and strained.

'I see,' he said, his own voice becoming strangely expressionless as his heavy lids dropped wearily. 'Your compassionate pretensions don't extend this far, do they, Cathy?'

She hung her head as she fastened her blouse, her dark hair falling like a curtain before her eyes. 'I don't know what you mean,' she said dully.

'You couldn't bring yourself to let a blind man make love to you.' She whipped round to face him in horror, his words cutting deep into her. 'You just couldn't do it. Disgust overcame your benevolent little dreams.' His face was almost frightening in its anger now, his black brows curving down over glittering eyes that seem to be looking into some inner furnace of passion.

'You know that's not true——'

'I should have known better,' he snarled, ignoring her faltering objection. 'God damn it, I should have known better than!' He rose to his feet in one fluid movement. 'Listen, Cathy,' he said grimly, 'I may be blind, but I'm still a man. My body still has a man's needs and reactions.' His eyes blazed suddenly, making her shrink away from him. 'I'm not a useless cripple, Cathy! And don't ever do this to me again—or blind as I am, I'll make you regret it for a long time to come.'

'I didn't want this to happen,' she quavered.

'Like hell you didn't!' Disbelief and hatred made his whole splendid physique taut and dangerous as he turned away from her. 'Either you haven't got the brains you were born with, or you're the sort of woman who enjoys teasing a chained bear——' In two swift steps he had reached her, big hands grasping for her, finding her arms, making her cry in the pain of his steel grip. 'I'm a man, Cathy, not an animal!'

'You started it,' she protested, close to hysteria. 'You did! God, don't you think I'm aching, too? Don't you know how this is tearing me inside? Oh, Fabian——'

She clung to him, pressing her wet cheeks against his chest, trying to muffle her sobs against his chest. He thrust her away, as though her touch had burned him like white-hot iron.

'What are you trying to do, damn you? Unman me completely? Don't you know when enough is enough?'

Cathy covered her face, her throat aching with the tears welling up from inside her. 'I can't work you out, Cathy,' he said, his voice gentler now, though still rough with passion. 'Why do you do this? You're such a crazy child sometimes—at other times such a wonderful, desirable woman——' He made as if to reach out for her, then checked himself. 'What's it all about, hmm? You must have been made love to before. You must know what this does to a man.' His eyebrows tightened. 'Or don't you?' She was silent, unable to answer. Slowly, his frown cleared. 'Is that it? You're a virgin?'

She nodded, and somehow he caught the motion.

'You're nodding. Oh, lord—I might have known.' He bit his lip with sharp white teeth, shaking his head. 'I should have remembered. When you first came into my office, I remember thinking how pure you looked, how virginal. As though what you'd done was somehow nothing to do with the real you. I'd forgotten that.' He sighed. 'I'd forgotten completely.' In the silence, the meadowlark sang its achingly sweet note. Slowly, he reached out his hand to her, a wry cleft appearing at one corner of his mouth. 'Silly girl! Little virgins oughtn't to be out alone in the woods with grown men. Not even blind men.'

Cathy took his hand in both of hers, too upset to speak, and laid her cheek against his knuckles. Gently he withdrew his hand, and laughed softly, ironically, to himself.

'So ends a perfect day. Well, like you said—let's get back to the house. Your father's waiting for his chess game.' He winced, pressing his fists to his supple waist, and bent forward.

'Are you hurt?' she asked anxiously.

'A slight ache,' he replied with quiet sarcasm. 'I must have over-exerted myself.'

His meaning brought the scarlet to her cheeks, and she came to his side in quick remorse.

'I'm so sorry, Fabian——'

He drew her to him, and held her close as he kissed her one last time, so fiercely that she thought she could taste blood on her lips. Her pulses surged at once, bringing the sweet, sick ache into her loins like a well-remembered fever.

'That's just to remind you of what might have been,' he growled, his eyes wintry. He released her. 'Now, do me a favour, and bring my horse here, will you?'

He didn't speak as they rode slowly back towards the meadows.

What a strange path her life had taken to reach this point! From that shocking revelation at Timothy Coryat's flat, through her bizarre episode with *Caprice*, her first meeting with Fabian Blackthorne, the horror and pain of his accident—to this sunny day, it had been a story marked by three things.

Mistakes, misjudgments and misunderstandings.

Over the next two or three days life at Northwood was charged with tension for Cathy.

If her father noticed that relations between his daughter and the young lawyer were strained, though, he showed no sign.

In fact, Dad was more cheerful than she had seen him in years. Fabian's company obviously stimulated him, and Fabian's powerful intellect—she never stopped being amazed at his ability to play excellent chess blind, or his incredible memory—was more a match for her father than her own could ever be. Towards Sir Cedric he was gentle, fast becoming a wry, amusing friend.

Towards Cathy he was scrupulously polite, no more. Yet under the politeness she sensed a tension that was almost savage. In her heart she knew that he despised her. *Shallow and childish*, those had been his words, and they still stung. To that judgment he had now clearly added, *sexual tease*.

Thinking it over, she couldn't really blame him. Stupidly, she had allowed him to form a judgment of her that was grossly unfair—and yet logical. Posing for a girlie magazine, wearing nothing but a red straw hat. Making a silly display of her feelings towards him. Going with him to the brink of sexual fulfilment, and then drawing back at the last minute. It all added up to a picture of a promiscuous fool, a shallow child's mind in a woman's body. The thought depressed her utterly.

The clash with Fabian in the woods had left her shaken, more shaken than perhaps she even realised.

On top of it all, she thought bleakly as she drove

back from Kaspar's to the hospital on Thursday afternoon, was the question of his blindness. Three more visits to the specialists had brought no further news. And she hadn't even been aware of her desperate hopes until the negative reports had dashed them every time. Heaven alone knew what Fabian must have felt.

It was so difficult to find a way into his mind. What he thought about his blindness, how he dealt with the depression and horror which must surely haunt him, was still hard to tell. And whenever she proffered the slightest sympathy, he reacted with a tense anger that whipped the colour from her cheeks.

Yet she was drawing closer to him than she had ever been.

It had taken her weeks to guess at the passionate pride in the man, the fierce male pride that he would defend as closely as his life itself. The pride that her clumsy sympathy trespassed upon.

She was coming to know him—but slowly. And painfully. A wry smile tugged at her gentle mouth as she pulled up on the gravel outside the Addington. He was so beautiful, as physically beautiful as a stallion, or any great male creature. Like the black panther of her dream. And yet his stunning attraction sometimes made her forget how brilliant his mind was, how proud his spirit was. And it was his spirit that she had come to love, with an irresistible love that made her yearn for him with every fibre of her being, every second of her life.

It was not arrogance, she thought, switching off the engine. More a kind of haughtiness—an assurance that came from an instinctive knowledge that he was above and beyond other men. Incomparable. She closed dreamy eyes as the thought of him brought back the slow, dizzying surge of passion back into the pit of her stomach. Blind or not, he was the most devastating, the most desirable, the most awe-inspiring man she had ever known. If only she could get that through to him. Dear heaven, if only she could show him that . . .

It was a wrench to part from her thoughts of Fabian

to walk into the Victorian mansion that served as one of the most progressive children's hospitals in Britain. Fortunately, Oliver Holland wasn't on duty. She couldn't have borne his importunate efforts to woo her right then. Instead, the doctor on duty was an old friend, Andrea Lorenz. Despite her petite, youthful appearance, the German psychiatrist had nearly fifteen years' of experience working with disturbed children. It was she who had realised that Cathy Milner's art lessons were not just entertainment for the children, but were evolving into a very valuable and important form of therapy.

Cathy always avoided discussing her work with Oliver. He was somehow too shallow. But with Andrea Lorenz she could discuss each child, her work in general, with complete frankness, and know that she always had a receptive and understanding ear. Andrea's smooth brown face had always reminded Cathy of a very intelligent monkey's. In the nicest way, of course!

'It's good to see you,' Andrea beamed. 'Are you all right, Catherine? The children are waiting for you eagerly.'

'I'm fine. How's Franz?'

'My husband works too hard,' Andrea smiled. 'But then so do I. I hear that your father is improving?'

'He's much better.'

'And that you have a guest at Northwood?' Andrea's brown eyes weren't inquisitive, merely warm. Cathy nodded.

'Fabian Blackthorne. He's a friend of the family. He was blinded in a car crash some weeks ago,' She grimaced, having never found it easy to say those words. 'He's still recuperating with Dad and me.'

'It's a very difficult situation,' Andrea nodded. 'You won't find it easy, and neither will he.' She turned to Cathy as they paused at the door of the ward. 'You will let me know? If there's anything I can do to help, that is. Sometimes a little friendly conversation can work wonders.'

Could Andrea sense the tension in her? Cathy

wondered. She nodded, feeling warmth for the calm, slim woman in front of her. 'I will,' she promised.

'Good,' Andrea Lorenz nodded briskly. 'And what are you going to do with your children this afternoon?'

'I thought I'd try and get them to paint feelings,' Cathy said, consulting the notes she had jotted in what she called her 'Addington File'. 'Anger, sorrow, loneliness, happiness, tranquillity—that sort of thing.' She hesitated. 'I had an idea it might help them to organise their thoughts, maybe even to release things they might have bottled up inside for a long time.'

'An excellent idea,' said Andrea, her brown face showing real pleasure. 'Truly excellent, Catherine. I've said this before—you should become a psychologist, a child psychologist. You would go far.'

'I'm not a clever person,' Cathy smiled, though pleased with the compliment. 'Not like you or Oliver. I'm a dabbler. Still, who can tell?'

'Exactly. Who can tell?' Smiling, Andrea pushed open the door, and Cathy walked through to face the usual tempestuous greeting from her young class. Andrea Lorenz took up a discreet position at the back of the classroom, and Cathy set to work at once.

It was a relief, really, to be able to push Fabian to the back of her mind for an hour and a half. He had loomed so large in her life lately, and so much had depended upon him, that she had had little time to think of anything else. The children were responsive, even John-Paul, who absorbed himself in a disturbing sketch of a stick figure in the midst of red flames.

'When I'm angry,' he said simply, passing the still wet painting to Cathy.

As always, it was hard for her to resist Ursula, the little Downes Syndrome girl. Jean Robson, the nurse, had tied her pigtails high on the sides of her head to keep them out of the way of paint; and this gave her little Mongol face a quaintly raffish appearance. She nestled by Cathy's side, hunched over a gleaming sheet of paper which she was covering with a deep blue sky, white clouds, and dozens of Y-shaped birds. She called the painting, 'When I feel peaceful.' Deeply touched, Cathy applauded her effort gently. Why was it that little Ursie found so rapid a way into her heart? She felt towards the child almost as a mother—or at least, an older sister. She had to tear herself away from Ursula to watch over what the other children were doing, guiding errant paintbrushes, making gentle suggestions.

Excitement was high. Andrea Lorenz watched with a faint smile and thought how pretty Cathy was, with that black hair and those striking green eyes. Such a pity the blind man at Northwood couldn't see her. And Cathy was skilled, too. She could sometimes bring out more in these children than any psychotherapy or drugs.

'If only we psychiatrists could be as spontaneous as you,' she said enviously to Cathy during a break. 'It's a rare quality. If only we could stop being *Doctor* to these children, and start being *friend*, we might get somewhere. Whatever happens,' she said firmly, 'we mustn't lose you, Cathy. For many of these children, you're the only way out. I really wish you'd think about a psychology degree.'

'We'll see,' promised Cathy—but was already absorbed in her work again.

She did her best to guide, rather than dominate. And as always, her stimulation brought the children's inmost feelings out, revealing deep sources of joy or satisfaction, and sometimes releasing the nightmares that could terrorise a child's mind. Inevitably, the session drew to an end, and Jean Robson intervened to help Cathy clear up the mess, store the paintings to dry, and get the children to clean up ready for their tea.

All protested vigorously—but an hour and a half was the optimum time, Cathy had worked that out a long time ago. Anything further was overtiring, and she was adamant.

'Goodbye, Cathy,' said Ursula, clinging to her neck with soapy hands. 'I'll miss you. Come soon.' Cathy hugged the unco-ordinated little body as hard as she dared, as if by the strength of her embrace she could tell the child how much she loved her, how much she cared. There was a lump in her throat as she watched the pigtailed figure trot away. In the end, she thought wryly, words don't mean much, do they? It's only through hugs and kisses that we communicate with the world of sick children.

She rinsed her own hands in the basin. Amazing how much paint managed to find its way into her hair and on to her clothes. Andrea Lorenz came up with a towel, her glasses dangling round her neck by their gold chain. Her brown monkey face was smiling.

'You love that little girl, don't you?' she said gently as Cathy dried her arms.

'Ursula?' Cathy nodded. 'She's a little angel. Somehow, she gets right through to me. I try and tell myself to stay professional, distanced—but it's no good. One grin from her, and my heart melts.'

'That's your strength, Cathy, not your weakness. The Downes Syndrome children are the sweetest of the sweet. You could eat her up, couldn't you?'

They strolled up to the staff canteen for a reviving cup of coffee. Andrea was watching Cathy's face carefully.

'If you wanted to,' she began hesitantly, 'you could have her now and then, for weekends.'

'Ursie?' Cathy's face expressed mixed emotions. 'I'd love that, really I would. But I might get just a little bit too attached. In a way, I'm almost afraid . . .'

'I understand. But if you have a special empathy with one child, Catherine, you might as well exploit that fully. It won't harm the others. And it could only do Ursula good.' She smiled. 'The question is whether *you* could stand it.'

'Maybe.' She took the coffee that Andrea passed her. 'Maybe when my father's a little stronger——' She made her mind up. 'Yes,' she beamed. 'Yes—when Dad's better, I'll take her home for the weekend.'

'Good—*sehr gut*! Let's sit and talk.'

Leaning back in the sofa, Cathy shook her head. 'If Ursula was *my* child, Andrea, I could never part with her. Never. No matter what was wrong with her, no matter how much time and love it took. I just couldn't do it.

'You don't get to read their files,' Andrea Lorenz said with a sigh. 'The things that some parents do are enough to make the angels weep. The amount of human tragedy within this hospital would fill libraries, Catherine.' She sipped her coffee. 'The mothers are as bad as the fathers. In some ways, they can be worse. But not everyone can cope with a subnormal or brain-damaged child. For some the drain on time and emotion is simply too great—and it's far better they let the professionals like us care for the children than struggle along on their own, locked in misery.'

'I suppose so,' Cathy agreed thoughtfully.

'As a matter of fact—though I shouldn't tell you this—Ursula does have a mother. I believe she tried to care for Ursula for the first year, and then gave up. Ursula's been with us for eleven years now.' Andrea hesitated. 'The mother used to get overwrought, frustrated, violent. She told me once that she was afraid she would have harmed the child if she hadn't passed her on to the Addington. Apparently she beat her once or twice.'

Cathy winced. 'Who could have the heart to hurt Ursie?'

'It's human nature to be impatient,' Andrea said drily. 'So you see, it was much better that the mother didn't keep her. She comes to see her daughter sometimes—not often—and gets very emotional. She also leaves very generous donations. But enough of that. Now tell me about *your* patient—Mr Blackthorne, is it? How did you get to know him?'

'In a rather roundabout way,' Cathy said with a confused smile. 'I went to him—well, I went to him for some help.'

'He's a doctor?'

'A lawyer. I got into some trouble a few weeks ago, and he got me out of it. He's also been helping my father with some minor worries.'

'And because of this, you're now looking after him?'

'Basically, I suppose so.'

'The trouble he got you out of must have been great for you to feel so obliged to him,' said Andrea, and again there was no curiosity in her voice, only serious concern.

'I made rather a fool of myself,' she admitted. 'It would have turned out badly for me.'

'Something to do with your ex-fiancé? Timothy?'

'Yes.' And then, without even pausing to think, she was spilling the whole story out to Andrea. The wide room was deserted, and the late afternoon sunlight was making lazy pools on the carpet. Outside, the noises of children at play came faintly to them—but neither woman listened. Andrea Lorenz sat in silence, merely nodding from time to time; and Cathy told her everything. About the horror of what she had seen at Tim's flat. About the whisky she had drunk. The bizarre idea that had burst into her grief. About the studio, the lights, the way she had posed, the thoughts that had whirled through her mind.

And then about what Fabian had done for her. And about his relationship with Cerise Hunniford, her own jealousy and the final catastrophe of Fabian's accident.

Drained, she came to a halt. 'I guess you hear some strange stories,' she said tiredly. 'Are you disgusted with me?'

'For posing in the nude?' For the first time in an hour Andrea shifted in her seat, and smiled. 'No. As a matter of fact, it isn't such a crazy reaction as you think. It was, at least, a way of expressing your feelings. And, like everything else you do, my dear Catherine, it was original.' She laughed softly, 'Okay, so it wasn't very sensible. But doing what you did probably averted what could have been a very nasty breakdown. And believe me, what you did wasn't so terribly unusual. A psychiatrist would understand. Maybe most people would, if they gave it a little thought.'

'Really?' Cathy's oval face expressed tentative relief. 'Do you mean that?'

'Of course.' Andrea reached out to pat Cathy's hands.

'Silly child—who would suspect you of being immoral? But let's turn to your friend for the moment—Fabian. He sounds like an exceptional man.'

'He is,' Cathy said ruefully.

'And like most exceptional people, difficult. No matter how courageous he may be, Cathy, he needs help. He can't handle this on his own. And there's a limit to what you can do for him, especially if he's proud. And *especially* if, as I rather suspect, your feelings for him are more those of a lover than a nurse.' Cathy flushed, twisting her hands, and Andrea nodded. 'I thought so. And how does he feel about you?'

'He says I'm shallow and childish,' Cathy said mournfully. 'And on top of that, he thinks I'm insincere about him. I don't think he likes me very much.'

'Okay, I won't go any further. It's not my business.' Andrea let her glasses drop on their thin chain, making a valley between her small breasts, and ran her slim fingers through the cap of her dark hair. 'But Fabian needs to talk to someone who has experience of dealing with the blind.'

'Would you speak to him?' Cathy ventured.

'Of course—if he'll listen to me. But I'd really like him to see a colleague of mine, Conrad Sikorski. Conrad is literally a genius, Cathy. He deals with the blind, the deaf, all kinds of handicapped people.' The word *handicapped* made Cathy wince inside, but she suppressed the feeling.

'Yes,' she nodded, 'you're right. Of course Fabian must see someone. Look, why not come round to dinner some time this weekend? Maybe you can persuade him that Conrad Sikorski will be able to help. Maybe you'll be able to get past that stubborn will of his.'

'Maybe,' Andrea smiled. 'Shall we say Sunday night?'

'Oh, I look forward to that!'

'*Ausgezeichnet*–excellent. I, too, look forward to meeting your superman. And Catherine——'

'Yes?'

'About that episode with the photographs—don't make a big deal out of it. Okay? What you did was understandable, maybe even natural. And it's all over now. The pictures went in the fire, remember? Put the memories and the guilt there too.'

'Yes,' said Cathy slowly, 'maybe I'll do exactly that.'

CHAPTER EIGHT

'WHY not?' Fabian had demanded. 'Have you got anything better to do? Well then, let's go. If I spill wine down my shirt, you can always mop it up for me.'

And she was still blinking in nervous disbelief on Friday evening as an unctuous waiter ushered them to a discreet table in an alcove lit by two rose candles.

Cathy's father had decided to undertake his first bit of Parliamentary work since his attack, and was attending a party conference in Brighton. He was going to be away the whole weekend. Fabian's idea that the two of them should go out to one of London's best restaurants had arrived with characteristic suddenness, and she had laughingly allowed him to sweep her off, intrigued by his bright courage.

Now, making their way gingerly to their alcove, Cathy was deeply glad they had come. From the corner of her eye, she watched the heads turn to stare at Fabian as they passed. The stares fell into a pattern, she realised with dry amusement—an instant flutter of feminine interest, an appraisal of the stunning face and magnificent animal physique. Then some attempt to catch his attention. And then the slow puzzlement, the growing realisation of what his deliberate care meant. Why those dazzling eyes didn't register. At which point the glazed look generally set in . . .

'It sounds crowded,' commented Fabian as they took their seats.

'It is,' she supplied. 'And you're getting a lot of female attention, if you're interested.'

'I'm not,' he said briefly. 'Have they given us a good table?'

'The best. And this is supposed to be the best restaurant in London right now. I'm looking forward to having my senses assailed with rich herbs and garlic.'

'Just don't breathe on me afterwards.' The waiter who materialised at Fabian's elbow listened attentively as Fabian ordered a vintage champagne to start. It was almost impossible to tell that he was blind, she thought. He carried so much natural authority, so much class and distinction; once again she marvelled at his courage in deciding to take her out to dinner in one of the most famous restaurants in London, bare months after losing his sight.

'Some people make a fuss about fifteen-year-old champagne,' he told her as the waiter evaporated. 'Personally, I prefer my champagne to be fresh, youthful and sparkling. Which is also, incidentally, the way I prefer my lovers.' His smile was as dry as the champagne would no doubt be, and she grinned in return, slowly growing used to his teasing humour. 'What a pity I can't see you,' he mused, his fierce grey eyes searching for her image through narrowed, thick-lashed lids. 'Are you stupefyingly beautiful tonight?'

'Simple but classy, I'd say,' she smiled. 'And very little make-up, just the way you like it.'

'I didn't say I didn't like make-up. I just said it tasted awful.'

'Well, you'll be pleasantly surprised if you intend to taste me tonight,' she said. But she couldn't carry off the remark the way she would like to have done, and a scarlet tide swept into her cheeks. He rumbled with laughter.

'I sincerely hope you're not blushing, my dear Cathy—or you'll be ruining the whole effect of sophistication.'

'I'm not,' she assured him. He reached out, and laid his knuckles against her cheek.

'Liar.'

The arrival of the champagne spared her further embarrassment, and she watched in relief as the golden wine sparkled into the tulip glasses. Fabian was quieter, more at peace, than she had seen him in weeks. He toasted her silently, and drank the champagne reflectively, his eyes brooding.

'I've invited a friend to dinner this weekend,' she said, deciding to break the subject of Andrea Lorenz in advance. 'She's very keen to meet you.'

'Oh?' His stare would have been formidable if he had been able to see her. 'Who is she?'

'She's called Andrea Lorenz.'

'Okay, let me guess. Some kind of social worker?'

'No,' she replied, wincing at the instant aggression in his face. 'As a matter of fact, she's a psychologist, a very gifted child psychologist.' To her surprise, Fabian broke into a soft laugh.

'So, I'm not only blind, but crazy as well!'

'It's not like that, Fabian.' She paused as the waiter placed their taramasalata on the table, then went on. 'She's simply a friend, nothing more.'

'And how did you come to make friends with a child psychologist?' he asked drily. She passed him Melba toast, and placed a knife in his fingers. The brief contact with his warm skin made her heart jolt like a schoolgirl's—as always. She kept her voice neutral.

'Andrea works at the Addington Hospital. I help out there now and then.'

'The children's hospital?' His eyebrows arched. 'What do you mean, "help out"?'

'Nothing much,' she shrugged. It was so difficult to describe her work there to anyone; and with Fabian, who might mock her without mercy, she was utterly tongue-tied. 'I just go there twice a week. To—well, to sort of entertain the children. Give the nurses a break.'

Fabian ate in silence for a while.

'I see,' he said at last. 'So you're not entirely useless.'

'Not entirely,' she agreed flippantly.

'What do you do, exactly? To entertain them, I mean?'

'Well——' she floundered, 'I run a sort of art class. I try and teach them how to use paint and crayons—the better co-ordinated ones, that is.'

'Curiouser and curiouser.' His face was thoughtful. 'This is the first I've heard of your sideline in child welfare. How did you get into it?'

'Well,' she began awkwardly, 'I had a friend at school whose younger sister was in the Addington. I used to go with her sometimes on visits. I must have been about sixteen, I suppose. Somehow, the place fascinated me—not in a morbid way, but because there were so many opportunities there.'

'Opportunities to do what?'

'To help. Opportunities for the children there to be taken a little out of their problems, maybe shown ways of helping themselves. I had the idea for months, really. But I didn't start doing anything about it until Mum went off with that Frenchman——'

'What idea?' he probed.

'Oh,' she said, feeling hot, 'it's too silly to talk about. Let's try a less boring topic.'

'I'm not bored,' he said gravely. 'What was your idea?'

'It wasn't exactly original,' she shrugged, feeling distinctly foolish. 'It just occurred to me that drawing and painting could become a very important part of these children's lives. I mean, art has always been used as a way of looking into someone's mind. You ask a child to draw its parents, and by studying the drawing you get some idea of what that child feels about its home situation. What I wanted to do was something else—to teach the children *real* skills. To try and show them how they could use art to express themselves. Almost anyone can make some kind of a mark on a piece of paper—and that mark, whatever it is, could represent a real achievement for, say, an autistic child who couldn't use words. Or idiot children who couldn't learn more complicated skills.' She broke off, realising that she'd grown quite excited. Why make a fool of yourself? she asked herself grimly. He'll do a much better job for you.

'Go on,' he commanded.

'I don't know what else to say. I took my idea to the supervisor of the hospital while I was still in my first year of college. That was after Mum had left. Maybe it was even *because* Mum had left, I don't know. Maybe I needed some kind of outlet.'

'And the supervisor liked the idea?'

'He was willing to try it out. So I started going there twice a week. You don't really want to hear any of this, do you?'

'Oh, but I do,' Fabian said softly. 'How did things go at first?'

'At first—rotten. The first six months were just chaos. It seemed to me that I was just wasting my time completely. I couldn't get the kids to do more than just make a mess. Nothing I tried to teach them seemed to sink in.' She grinned ruefully. 'I blamed them—but of course, it was me. I didn't have the skills to communicate with them. I didn't realise that it takes a lifetime to learn how to teach, let alone how to teach handicapped children. And after that first period, I slowly started noticing changes. What they were drawing and painting wasn't just mess any more—they were beginning to really express themselves, to find a way of communicating with the world. I can't tell you what that meant to me. I was so excited! I thought I'd really achieved something.'

'I can imagine,' he said. A slow, rare smile curved across his mouth. 'And now? Three years later?'

'Well, I know a bit more about what I'm doing. I'm still in the dark most of the time. But I've got somewhere, at least. The children are enjoying themselves immensely—and it seems to be doing them some good.' She looked up at him shyly. 'I suppose it all sounds rather silly and pointless to you.'

'What makes you play it down so much, Cathy? Why are you so afraid that I'm going to laugh at you?'

'Oh——' she toyed with her wine-glass, 'I don't know. Tim used to find the whole thing ridiculous. I got him to go along to one of the classes once, but he just got bored and said nasty things. And you——' She broke off.

'I've been pretty savage to you, is that it?'

'In a way.' She watched the quiet smile on that passionate, sensual mouth. 'Well?' she challenged. '*Do* you find it silly and pointless?'

'No, I find it brave—and touching. And very, very perceptive. But then you're a very perceptive woman, aren't you, Cathy? You see into everyone's heart, maybe a little too clearly for comfort sometimes. Which makes certain people—certain bitter, cynical, twisted people—react harshly sometimes. And call you shallow. But you're not shallow, my sweet one. You're about as shallow as the Pacific.' Long before he had finished, a flaming blush had suffused her cheeks and throat, and she slopped champagne on to the crisp white tablecloth as her fingers tightened round the fragile stem of her glass.

Fabian reached for her hand and drew her fingers up to his mouth with that same dizzyingly intimate smile. She sat in a mixture of joy and terror as he kissed her fingertips with warm, gentle lips—then the sensitive hollow of her palm—then the fluttering pulse inside her wrist. His smile deepened.

'You're wearing *Chamade* again.'

'You said you liked it,' she said huskily, hardly trusting herself to speak.

'I do. It suits you.' He let his long lashes close over diamond-bright eyes as he inhaled the scent on her skin. 'Mysterious, alluring—it suits you. You should always wear it.'

'Wow,' she said shakily as he restored her trembling fingers to her, 'this is a change from being shallow and childish. I'm not sure if I can take it.'

'People who are in pain and fear sometimes turn on those who are closest to them,' he said obliquely. 'It's impossible to explain, and I'm not going to try. Not tonight, anyway. Now,' he went on quietly, 'over the next course I want to hear everything about your work at the Addington. You hear me? Everything.'

'I don't know where to begin,' she stammered.

'Begin at the beginning,' he commanded. 'With the day your mother left for France.'

'You really want to hear about it?' she asked. 'All right. Just stop me if I get too boring.' And slowly, full of hesitations at first, she began telling him about the past three years of her life. Not just the surface detail, but the inside story, the story of her feelings and experiences. Her triumphs, her moments of despair. The growing maturity that had helped her deal with one of the most difficult phases in her life; the problems with Timothy Coryat; her deepening relationship with the children at the Addington; Kaspar Aprahamian, at whose shop she had worked as much because she loved the old man as because she loved the rich beauty of his wares. And Fabian listened quietly, throwing in a question now and then, nodding silently at other times, always attentive, always seeming to understand what she was saying, the meanings she tried to bring out.

'Do you look like your mother?' he asked at one stage.

'Well, I've got her hair and colouring, I suppose. But my eyes are more like my father's. My mother is tall and willowy—I'm short and squat.'

'From what I remember of you,' he said with a wicked glint, 'you'll do fine. And you can afford another helping of these delicious potatoes.'

It was over the redolent fruit cocktail, as several parties of late diners had begun to arrive from plays and films, that Cathy's words suddenly dried up in her throat. Fabian's eyes narrowed.

'What is it?'

'A friend of yours.' She looked bleakly at the redhaired woman who was slipping off a mink cape near the door, her perfectly made up face vivacious as she talked to her companion. 'Cerise Hunniford. And friend.'

'Indeed?' Fabian looked unperturbed. Cathy glanced towards the door again, and the sharp blue eyes met hers with a flash of recognition. For an instant, Cathy could sense that Cerise was hesitating, struggling with herself. And then her heart sank. Cerise was stalking their way, her arm firmly clasped through her companion's, a handsome Middle Easterner obviously five or six years younger than herself.

'Well,' said Cerise, with artificial brightness as she

reached them, 'Fabian and the delectable Miss Milner. How delightful to see you both!'

'Hullo, Cerise,' Fabian said calmly, turning towards her. 'Are you well?'

'Never better.' Cerise's eyes flickered restlessly between Cathy and Fabian, though her mouth continued to wear an expression of mockery. 'Aphrodite Publications continue to reach new peaks. May I present my friend? This is Kassim.' The handsome young man shook Fabian's hand, and with perfect Arab manners, kissed Cathy's. Cerise watched Fabian, a strange, tense expression in her eyes.

'So,' she said with the same artificial gaiety, 'how have you been, Fabian?'

'As you see me.' He leaned back in his chair, the handsomest man in the room—and by far the most authoritative. 'Some doors close. Others open.'

'So I see.' Cerise darted a glance of pure malice at Cathy. But not for long. She seemed unable to tear her eyes away from Fabian's face.

'Are you——' she hesitated, 'are you managing?'

'Managing what?' Fabian asked calmly. At which point Kassim turned to Cathy with some polite remark. Forced into small-talk, she struggled to hear what Cerise and Fabian were saying. She was trying to puzzle out Cerise's expression.

'I've been learning Braille,' Fabian was saying. Unlike Cerise, he seemed totally undisturbed by the meeting. 'And I use tape-recorders a lot. I certainly don't intend to give up my career. And you? Prospering?'

'Making a fortune,' Cerise replied with a brittle laugh. She shot another glance at Cathy, who was politely trying to follow Kassim's compliments about the English countryside while listening with half an ear to the others. 'I hear you and Cathy Milner are now living together?'

'I'm staying at Northwood,' Fabian corrected. 'My father is in no condition to have me just now, so Cathy and her father have offered me a room in their house.'

'What else have they offered you?' she asked sourly.

'Are you trying to find out whether Cathy's my lover?' Fabian's voice was quiet. 'The answer is that it's none of your business, Cerise.'

'Why should I care?' retorted Cerise. She slid her arm possessively through Kassim's, nestling up to him provocatively. The gesture was lost on Fabian, who merely shrugged.

'Shall we go to our table, my Cerise?' the Arab suggested gently.

'Sure, lover.' But again she gave the impression that it was an effort for her to drag her troubled gaze away from Fabian. And then Cathy realised what that tense look meant. It meant that for all her flippancy, Cerise Hunniford still cared about Fabian—a great deal Which also explained the smile of pure hate that Cerise now gave Cathy.

'Posed for any more postcards?' she asked sweetly. 'You must let me know how your modelling career is going, darling—maybe we could use you again some time.'

The reference was lost on Kassim, but the acid in her words was perfectly intelligible to him. Firmly, with a grave smile, he eased Cerise away from the table.

'Goodbye, Fabian,' she said as she left, and the tremor in her falsely-gay voice was just audible. 'Take care.' Fabian merely smiled in her general direction, and turned back to Cathy.

'How about some coffee?'

'No, thanks.' Seeing Cerise again had upset her, brought back some of the old shadows. It was almost a surprise to discover that she was still so bitterly jealous of Cerise, and so acutely conscious of Cerise's bitter jealousy in return. She looked into Fabian's face with deep green eyes. So many women want you, my sweet, she thought silently. So many of us love you, the good, the bad, the beautiful, the plain. But who do you love? Or are you impervious to such soft feelings, stainless steel right through?

'What is it?' He drained the glass. 'Did Cerise disturb you?'

'I hate to admit it, but yes,' Cathy confessed. She chewed her lip for a second, then went on, 'She still feels a lot for you, Fabian.'

'I know.'

'Intuition?' she asked drily.

'A man can always sense when a woman cares about him,' he said indifferently.

'Oh.' In which case, she said silently, you must know all about this ache in my heart, this yearning, this jealousy, this fierce longing which I call caring. And which is the closest thing to pain that could reasonably be called pleasure. 'And you? You didn't treat her very warmly.'

'It wouldn't have helped her if I had,' he said, and ordered coffee and two brandies from the waiter who had come to clear the plates away. 'It's better that she simply gets over it.'

'She's not my favourite person,' said Cathy through clenched teeth, watching Cerise make a great show of holding her friend's hand across the room.

'She's not what anyone would call moral,' he said quietly. 'But she feels deeply. Her life hasn't been easy.'

'*Were* you her lover?' Cathy asked suddenly, before she had time to stop the question from coming out. For a moment she thought she was in line for a monumental snub; and then he smiled.

'What do you think?'

'I think——' she stared into the cloudy grey eyes as if the answer lay there, somewhere in those crystal depths, 'I think you must have been. Cerise wouldn't have found you so hard to forget otherwise.'

'Hmm.' He didn't confirm or deny her guess. 'Why should I be so special? Cerise Hunniford has had many lovers.'

'I don't imagine you would be difficult to remember,' Cathy rejoined wryly, and his mocking smile deepened.

'Indeed? You must be psychic, then, to be able to tell what sort of lover a man is just by looking at him.'

'I've got no idea what sort of lover you are,' she said hotly. 'You twist my words deliberately. I just meant that you're intelligent, charming——' She gave up in the face of his soft chuckle. She hated him to tease her like this, and her temper was fraying nervously as her pleasure in the evening evaporated. Unburdening her secret thoughts to him had left her feeling slightly drained, anxious that she had over-committed herself to him. On top of that, Cerise's presence in the restaurant was a niggling worry that she could have done without. It was a constant strain to be with the man she loved more than anyone else in the world, yet to be so uncertain, so lacking in self-confidence.

She drank her brandy in a moody silence, beginning to regret having told Fabian so much of her personal history. The moment of intense warmth between them seemed to be over. It had been so sweet, so precious— yet now, it seemed, he was once more as indifferent to her as before. Damn Cerise! Her arrival, Cathy was sure, had changed the mood subtly. The intimacy between them had evaporated as soon as Cerise's fluting voice had broken into their conversation. Maybe, despite what he had said, he too was still emotionally involved with Cerise Hunniford. Maybe he wanted Cerise as much as Cerise obviously wanted him. And if Cerise ever overcame her mental block about Fabian's blindness, Cathy was certain that she would take Fabian away from her. Away? She didn't have the slightest, frostiest hold on Fabian Blackthorne. Nothing.

Despite the warming effect of the brandy, she was suddenly cold right through. An Arctic wind was blowing in her heart, and as if Fabian sensed her mood, he suggested they return to Northwood. She agreed miserably, and her arm lay limply in the crook of his elbow as they walked to the car. She had caught Cerise's expression as they had left the restaurant. About equal parts of hate, envy, and longing, Cathy guessed. Shaken, not stirred. It was with a heavy heart that she drove Fabian, now as silent as she was, back to Northwood.

The old house was quiet as they let themselves in

through the great oak door. Her father was going to be at Brighton for the weekend, and the thought of being alone at Northwood with Fabian was suddenly disturbing. The moon was full again—how the months were sliding by—and through the leaded windows its beams lit the soft darkness. At the foot of the stairs, she turned to him uncertainly.

'I—I think I'd better turn in early.'

He simply shrugged. 'As you wish. I'm going to have a brandy before I turn in.'

'Goodnight, Fabian. And—thank you for tonight.'

He nodded brusquely, and walked away.

Cathy went upstairs, leaden-hearted, and undressed for bed. It had been such a strange evening, she reflected. She'd been so close to him, yet so far away. Elusive Fabian . . .

She curled up on her side, closing her eyes, seeing the scene at the restaurant projected on her eyelids. Sleep was far away, and she could hear the sounds of Fabian moving downstairs, and then his tread on the staircase coming up. His bedroom lay at the far end of the corridor, but she suddenly found herself praying that he would not pass her door by. His footsteps were quiet, as though he didn't want to disturb her. But then they paused at her doorway, and she heard his gentle knock with beating heart.

She sat up in bed, pulling up the blanket to cover her flimsy nightgown.

'Come in,' she called softly, and the door swung open. He was silhouetted against the light, two brandy-glasses cupped in his hand.

'I thought this might help you sleep. You seem depressed.'

'I—I'm fine. But it was a sweet thought. I will have one, thanks.' He closed the door behind him, and she took the balloon glass he offered her, switching on her bedside lamp. He sat on the bed beside her and relaxed, tugging his tie loose. He reached for her glass, clinked his own gravely against it, and gulped at the amber liquor.

'Now, what's the matter, Cathy? I told you not to get upset about Cerise Hunniford.'

'I'm not upset about anything,' she lied, tasting the brandy. 'I'm just tired.'

'You weren't tired half an hour ago. And you stopped talking about yourself. Why?'

'I must have been boring you stiff,' she said, looking away from his face. He was so beautiful, so masculine; looking into that blind face tugged painfully at her heartstrings.

'You know you weren't. Now what's upset you?'

'So many questions!' she exploded. 'Why can't you just leave me alone?' Eyes bright with tears, she grasped his lapels with both hands, vainly trying to shake him. 'Why can't you just——'

And then he was kissing her, his mouth fierce and sweet. Cathy clung to him like a drowning woman as his arms encircled her, crushing her slim body against him. She responded with a heady passion, her whole soul becoming a river in full flood, a torrent that was pouring itself into its sea. It was an ecstasy to be able to leave all thought, all worry, all fear behind her, and to be swept up in the magnificent power of his desire for her.

Lost in the deep fathoms of their embrace, Cathy strained against Fabian's warm, hard body, her fingers exploring his neck, his shoulders, the broad plane of his back, with restless hunger. When at last he tore his mouth away from hers, she was panting, her breath ragged in her dry throat.

'Oh, my love,' she whispered shakily, 'you devastate me.'

'I've been hungry for that for days.' His voice was deep and rough, and she thrilled to the bright fire in his eyes. 'Have you put the lights on?'

'The lights——' She tried to clear her whirling mind. 'Only the lamp beside you—but why——?'

Fabian reached behind to sweep the light out. In the darkness, black and velvety as a black jaguar's coat, his voice was a throbbing whisper. 'I want you to be on

equal terms with me—in the dark. No eyes, just touch.
And taste. And smell. And the sound of our two
voices.' She cried out low in her throat as he reached
for her, his hands sure and possessive in the darkness.
'Are you afraid, Cathy?'

'With you I'm afraid of nothing,' she whispered. She
arched her neck as his mouth found her throat, his lips
hot against the beating pulse of life there. Without
thought, her fingers were making their way through his
thick, crisp hair. The man-smell of him was in her
nostrils as he kissed her throat, the soft line of her jaw,
the sensitive skin beside her ear. She whispered his
name, again and again, and in return felt the taut
response of his arms around her.

'You're trembling,' he said, and she could hear the
smile in his velvety voice. And indeed, her heart seemed
to be fluttering in her breast like a bird against a
window. But her love for Fabian was a symphony in
her soul, a wild music that raged and crooned and
pounded inside her. In the darkness, her skin seemed to
have become shudderingly sensitive; there was no need
of words—the language of their bodies, of whispering
skin and beating hearts, said it all.

His lips brushed hers languorously, then with almost
savage male need, demanding her response with total
authority. Helpless, she melted against him. In her
dream it had never been like this—not a fraction as
sweet, as terrifying, as intoxicating.

He shrugged off his jacket, letting it slide to the floor,
and Cathy lay back weakly as he tore impatiently at the
buttons of the shirt.

'Tell me you didn't care for Cerise,' she begged in a
low voice. 'Tell me she doesn't matter to you.'

'Cerise has nothing to do with this,' he growled.
'Why think of her at all?'

And when he came to her again, his upper body was
naked. She had never known anything like this, the
reeling shock of his contact with her. His skin was hot
satin over pulsing steel, and she ran her hands shakily
from the rocky strength of his shoulders, down his

flanks to the supple, taut waist. Her touch made him gasp deep in his throat.

'Cathy, Cathy...' Their kiss was endlessly sweet as his fingers found the fastenings of her gown, exposing her body with barely controlled impatience. She tried to protest, but her body betrayed her, and she strained against him. Then, as he slid the silk off her shoulders, she slid bonelessly against the pillows, surrendering to his desire.

'I must know,' she whispered, her mouth against his. 'I must know whether you love Cerise Hunniford.'

'Little idiot!' She arched in his arms as his fingers stroked the full swell of her breasts. 'Why are you obsessed with Cerise?'

'Because I'm jealous,' she said shakily. 'Because I couldn't bear it if you still wanted her. If you were thinking of her when you kissed me...'

'My sweet fool, do you imagine I could think of anyone but you right now?'

'No, but——' His lips silenced her, and she was lost again, her breasts crushed against his hard chest. His hands slid hungrily down her naked back, tracing the line of her backbone, the delicate curves of her slender body. Mustering a last reserve of strength, she fought away from him—only to find that she was slipping helplessly on to her back. Her shoulder bumped something—her brandy glass, carelessly left on her bedside table—and it toppled, spilling warm brandy over skin. 'Damn!'

'Clumsy,' Fabian smiled. 'I'd never have been so careless—I've grown used to the dark, you see.'

'Well, I haven't,' she muttered. He leaned forward, and she felt his tongue taste the liquor on her breasts. A deep shudder made her throw her head back, her body straining to meet him as his lips traced the rivulet of brandy across the curve of her breast to her aching nipples...

'Brandy and Catherine.' His tongue was a sweet, fiery torment on the points of her breast, firming each bud into a peak of desire. 'I think it's just become my favourite drink. And so you see, there are certain advantages to losing one of your senses. The others become—how shall I put it? More refined.' His teeth were sharp, making her gasp in sudden passion. 'Did I hurt you?' he purred, his voice mocking.

'Your indifference hurts me,' she said softly, her fingers tracing the muscles of his shoulders, the tendons that shaped his neck. He raised himself.

'You think I'm indifferent to you.'

'You're so cool, so composed.' She drew a shuddering breath. 'You can do something as—erotic as that to me, and then tease me afterwards. That hurts, Fabian. Don't you feel *anything* for me?'

He was silent for a few seconds, then he leaned forward to kiss her lips softly. 'Yes, Cathy. Yes. I feel a great deal for you.'

Perhaps that was enough, she thought dreamily. Perhaps that was the best she could hope for. Slowly, so very slowly, she trailed her fingers over his man's body, exploring him, discovering the bone-melting potency of his need for her. And discovering, with almost frightened joy, her own power to give him pleasure, make him surge against her touch as fierce as the sea, as wild as a storm.

He kissed her with a searching tenderness that drugged her like hot wine, his arms drawing her tight against his nakedness. The infinite grace of their entwining was filled with a new power, an immediacy that no longer distinguished between man and woman, Cathy and Fabian. They were one, mouth to mouth, thigh against thigh, their fingers entwining, parting, exploring in the first wonderful dance of love.

The darkness was theirs. It no longer mattered that there had been pain, separation between them. Now all that mattered was the giving of delight, the almost overwhelming need to reach one another's secrets, offering pleasure, adoration, worship. He slid her clothes off with sure hands, his body delighting in hers with an intense passion that made her weak. His kisses drugged her senses like poppy-juice, his touch sealing a magic over her that turned her blood to molten gold. She was so ready for him, her readiness becoming desperate urgency, a driving force that had suddenly become the most important thing in the world.'

His breathing was harsh as he drew her to him, his hands cupping her hips as he pushed between her thighs. 'Cathy,' he groaned, deep in his chest, 'my sweet love, my heart, my soul . . .'

And as his body thrust into hers, a searing invasion that seemed to reach her very heart, she cried out aloud, her nails digging wildly into the muscles of his back. His potency was almost frightening, too full, too deep, and yet through the golden light that dazzled her mind she knew that for the first time in her life, she was fulfilled, for the first time she had known what love was.

They lay locked in that first embrace for slow seconds of fire, Fabian whispering her name against her moist skin again and again.

As he began to move, at first gentle, then powerful and demanding, she felt her spirit flooding with a fierce joy—joy that he was taking her at last, joy that she was becoming a woman in his arms. Her body was on the brink of a waterfall, she could hear the thunder of the falling waters, the irresistible current hauling her inevitably to the brink. She could feel his passion mounting to a head, ready to explode. 'Fabian,' she whispered, her body arching to his like a huntsman's bow, '*please*——'

His arms tightened like steel around her as he gasped her name. And then the waterfall had come, and with no control left, she was tumbling down the giddy heights, her body surging and spinning and sinking into the bright turbulent waters beneath . . .

The brightness ebbed away with infinite slowness, leaving her exhausted and drained. He slid off her, and she found herself cradled in his arms, the dark cloud of her hair spread out across his skin.

'I love you,' she whispered, clinging to him with spent arms. 'I always have done.'

'Hush,' he said quietly, caressing her hair. 'Did I hurt you?'

'No,' she whispered. She didn't cry often, but she was doing so now, for the sheer beauty of what had happened between them. Fabian pulled the bedclothes over her with the gentleness of a lover. Her bed was welcoming, the bed of her childhood, the bed of her womanhood. 'You won't need your *Bunty Annual* tonight,' he said softly, kissing her lips.

'How—do you know about that?' she breathed, her eyelids closing like lead over dreamy eyes.

'Your father tells me all your secrets.' He brushed the hair back from her forehead. 'Sleep now.'

'Don't go,' she begged.

'I won't.'

He held her in his arms until her breathing was slow and regular. Then brushed his lips against her cheek.

'Damn,' he whispered, almost too softly to be heard. 'Damn. And damn this darkness. If only I could see you now . . .'

When she awoke in the morning, he was gone.

It didn't surprise Cathy that Fabian and Andrea Lorenz should have taken an instant liking to each other, or that they should have slipped almost immediately into a talkative friendship.

What did surprise her was the sole topic of their conversation—herself.

As she brought the tray of sundown drinks out into the garden where Andrea, Fabian, her own father and Keith Blackthorne were relaxing in the twilight, she could hear Andrea's voice describing Cathy's art classes and the effect they had on the children. She winced in embarrassment. At least the two older men were happily involved in a discussion about golf. Both Keith Blackthorne and her father were looking better lately, she had noticed.

'In fact,' Andrea was concluding, 'Cathy has become an absolutely vital part of our work at the Addington. She's a part of the team now.'

'Spare my blushes,' Cathy said wryly as she dispensed glasses and ice.

'But it's true, Andrea assured Fabian. 'It's not just that her work helps us to see into the children's problems in a totally new way—she actually helps them to get better. She shows them how to express themselves, for one thing. But more than that, she brings them hope, brings a little light into their darkness.'

Fabian nodded. He had been listening intently, leaning back in his chair with his hands thrust into his pockets.

'It sounds as though Cathy should be a professional,' he said thoughtfully. 'Aren't there any specialist courses available?'

'There are. And I agree——'

'I don't,' said Cathy with an awkward laugh. 'I'm an amateur. I always will be.'

'An amateur.' Fabian savoured the word pensively. 'No, I don't think so. From what Andrea has told me, Cathy, you're a professional to your fingertips.'

'I just teach them how to paint,' she said. 'I don't have to know the complicated psychological theories behind what I do. I probably wouldn't even understand them. No, I'm happy being a dabbler.'

'Why do you run yourself down?' The grey eyes seemed to be looking straight into her heart, and she lowered her own lashes as though he could really see into her. The memory of their lovemaking ran like fire through her blood suddenly, bringing the colour flaring to her cheeks.

'Naturally,' Andrea put in, 'it's her decision. It's possible that formal training might just get in the way of what she does—I've considered that. I don't think so, though. Anyway,' she smiled, 'she's indispensable just as she is, and we all love her. Which reminds me— Oliver Holland sends warm greetings.'

'Thanks,' Cathy grimaced, and Fabian's eyebrows tilted.

'An admirer?'

'Oh, just a colleague,' Cathy said hastily.

'More than a colleague, surely,' said Andrea, much to Cathy's dismay. 'Oliver's quite besotted with Cathy. He never stops singing her praises. But that's understandable, isn't it?' She was so obviously probing for some reaction from Fabian that he couldn't help smiling.

'Yes,' he said gently, 'that's understandable. Cathy's an exceptional person.'

The word startled Cathy. Fabian thought her exceptional? Andrea Lorenz sent an assessing glance from Cathy to Fabian; then, as though satisfied with what she saw, touched Fabian's bare arm.

'Shall we take our drinks into the garden?'

'If you like.'

Knowing she wouldn't be wanted at this point, Cathy didn't join them, but remained listening to the interminable talk of golf from Keith and her father. She watched Fabian's lithe figure as he walked beside the petite psychiatrist down the avenue of rhododendrons. In all this time, his stride hadn't lost its confidence, its catlike grace. Perhaps, like some giant cat, he sensed his way around obstacles without need of sight? *Exceptional*. An exceptional person. The phrase lodged warmly in her mind. Had he really meant it? Or was it one of those polite things people said? She closed her eyes, remembering the feel of his body against hers. She had expected pleasure from lovemaking—but not the overwhelming, unforgettable experience of what they'd known in each others' arms. She was his now, his completely. She felt that as certainly as though they had been married in a church ... What mattered now was to plan for the future, try and guide Fabian towards the professional help that could make such a difference to his life—and hers. She prayed that Andrea would be able to persuade him to see Conrad Sikorski. If anyone could help Fabian adjust to his new life, the great scientist could.

It was almost dark by the time Fabian and Andrea had finished their quiet conversation, and were strolling back to the patio together.

'I suspected there was some plot afoot,' Fabian said grimly as they approached, and Cathy's heart sank. But then a smile crossed his face. 'Okay, I'll see Professor Sikorski. I've been persuaded that he might be able to help.'

She was able to stop herself from hugging him out of pure delight. Just.

And there was more good news from Andrea as she got into her car to drive home at the end of the evening.

'Oh, by the way, I've spoken to the Supervisor, and he's agreed to let you have Ursula for a weekend in a fortnight's time—if you're ready, that is.'

'I'm ready,' said Cathy happily, delighted at the prospect.

'It's not really orthodox—we should obtain her mother's consent. But since the mother almost never comes to see her, and since it's you—well, we're bending the rules a little. Happy?'

'Yes,' Cathy beamed. In her pleasure, she found she was hanging on to Fabian's powerful arm. 'Ursula's a Downes syndrome child,' she explained. 'What they sometimes call a Mongol. She's a real honey—you'll love her.'

'No doubt,' said Fabian with a smile. 'It was nice meeting you, Andrea.'

'It was more than nice meeting you,' Andrea Lorenz said quietly. 'I'll speak to Conrad first thing tomorrow, and arrange an initial meeting as soon as possible. Okay?'

Fabian lifted one hand in a gesture of surrender. 'Okay. If that's what Cathy really wants, I'll see the man.'

What *Cathy* really wants? For the second time that day, Cathy blinked up into Fabian's face in bewilderment. What persuasion had Andrea Lorenz used to convince him to see Sikorski? Surely Fabian didn't give a damn what Catherine Milner wanted?

Or did he?

The next few days passed rapidly. Late summer weather

gave way to a succession of rainstorms that drenched London. Cathy's car went into the garage for repairs. She saw Fabian hardly at all, since he was working tirelessly at mastering braille, and spent two nights at home with his father, whose health was improving. Andrea had arranged an appointment for him to see Conrad Sikorski towards the end of the week, and when Cathy met her at the Addington on Wednesday, she was full of praises for Fabian.

'A very courageous man,' she judged, 'but he will be all the more courageous for Conrad's help.'

'Tell me,' Cathy said thoughtfully, 'did you tell Fabian that it was *my* idea for him to meet Conrad Sikorski?'

'I thought it would help,' smiled Andrea.

'Why?'

'Because he obviously respects your opinions so much,' Andrea said in mild surprise. 'I knew he would agree if he thought you wanted it.'

'He doesn't respect my opinion at all,' Cathy blinked. 'I've told you, he thinks I'm barely grown up!'

'Yes?' Andrea's smile was whimsical. 'Well, it seems to have worked in this case, doesn't it?'

And that was that.

Fabian's appointment was for three-thirty on Thursday afternoon. To Cathy's anxiety, he insisted on taking the tube to the Harley Street surgery.

'I have to learn how to get around on my own,' he said firmly. 'I can't rely on your car for ever.'

'But you're not used to it—supposing you get lost——'

'I can always ask,' he smiled. 'And you're not picking me up from Harley Street, either. I'll come back the way I went.' The expression on his face silenced her protests, but it was with a heavy heart that she dropped him at the Northwood Tube station.

Heaviness had turned to fluctuating panic by evening. He should have returned hours ago! Cathy agonised over phoning the surgery, and when she finally plucked up the courage to find out whether Fabian had left, she was greeted only by an answering machine stating that Conrad Sikorski's clinic was now closed.

'He'll be perfectly all right,' her father chided gently. 'Fabian can look after himself.'

'But he's so late!' She checked her watch—after seven. 'He should have been back by now.'

'He's probably met a friend and gone for a drink. Men do, you know. He's been cooped up with you and me for the past ten days, after all—he's probably been bored stiff.' And when Cathy continued fretting, he retired behind his newspaper.

But she couldn't get the ghastly images out of her mind. Supposing he'd fallen under the train? Or been struck down by a car? Supposing he was lost, even now—too proud to ask directions . . . She sat clutching a novel in a cold sweat, telling herself not to be a damned fool. And cursing Fabian bitterly in between prayers for his safety. What was wrong with her? This nervous fever wasn't like her. She delayed dinner as late as possible—and couldn't eat a thing when she eventually did make it.

And it wasn't until eight o'clock that she heard a car's tyres crunch on the gravel outside.

'There,' Sir Cedric said calmly, 'I told you he'd be all right.'

She ran to the door with fluttering heart, and pulled it open—to see Fabian paying a taxi.

'Thank God!' she breathed, for once in her life really meaning the phrase. She ran to meet him, not caring how foolish she seemed, and threw herself into his arms.

'Hey! What's all this?' It was bliss to feel his broad chest against her, and she clung to him with shut eyes.

'I was worried,' she said, her words muffled against his chest. 'I didn't know what had happened—never, never do that again!'

'Well, well.' He stroked her hair gently, holding her close with his other arm. His voice expressed wonder. 'My poor baby! I had no idea you'd worry like this—I told you I'd make my own way home.'

'I know.' Sniffing, she clung tightly to him as they walked to the door. 'I missed you. Where on earth were you?'

'With Conrad Sikorski,' he said, sounding surprised.

'But I phoned his surgery, and they said it was closed!'

'We went into Guy's Hospital. Hullo, Cedric.'

'Hullo,' her father smiled. 'Have a good day?'

'Interesting,' Fabian said thoughtfully. 'I had a very interesting day.'

'I've kept some dinner for you,' said Cathy, going to fetch it as Fabian settled himself in the drawing room. How wonderful it was to be able to relax!

'Guy's?' she probed as she set the tray on his lap. 'Roast beef at six o'clock, potatoes at three, beans at nine, carrot at twelve. And water to your right.' It was a code they had learned at the Sark Institute to let him know where his food was. 'What did you go into Guy's hospital for?'

'Another brain-scan.' Calmly, he scooped meat into his mouth. 'God, I'm hungry! Medical science really seems to work up an appetite in me.'

'What did he want another brain-scan for?' Cedric Milner asked.

'Just a check-up. This food's good, Cathy. And how have you two spent the evening?'

'Worrying about you,' Sir Cedric said with a smile. 'So—was this Sikorski chap helpful?'

'Very,' Fabian nodded, his face thoughtful. 'He's full of bright ideas on how to adjust. Courses, classes, encounter groups—all that sort of thing. It all sounds like hard work, but probably very useful.'

'Ah well, as long as it does some good.' Cedric Milner glanced at Cathy, who was staring mistily at Fabian with adoring green eyes, and smiled to himself. 'Well,' he decided, hauling himself out of his chair, 'it's time I was heading for bed. Goodnight, children.' He closed the drawing-room door behind him as he left, and Fabian smiled.

'I like your father. He's a diplomat.'

'An M.P. has to be,' she said. 'The doctor says he'll be fit enough to go back to Parliament when the next session begins.'

'Good. And my father seems to be recovering from the shock of my little accident at last. I was worried about him, I don't mind telling you—he's not as strong as he was.' He pushed the empty plate aside, and leaned back against the cushions with a sigh. His face was still thoughtful, the dark brows descending over the bright eyes. She cleared the tray, and came back to him with coffee. He patted the seat next to him. 'Sit here. I want to talk to you.'

Her heart was filled with love as she settled beside him, the warmth of his body seeming to wrap her completely. To her surprise—and delight—he locked his fingers through her own, and held them tight.

'I've had quite an afternoon, Cathy.'

'Sikorski was interesting?'

'Yes, very. He's a brilliant man; you can sense that as soon as he comes into the same room. He has a kind of aura, I don't know how to describe it——'

'I think I know,' she smiled. 'So—why did he want you to have another scan?'

'It wasn't the usual thing.' She looked up at him swiftly. 'It was a C.A.T. scan. Axial Tomography, they call it. Some expensive new machine they've just installed.'

'And?'

'Well, according to this new machine, what's causing my blindness is a lesion. An area of scar tissue, caused by a ruptured blood vessel. The way that Sikorski described it, it's rather like a spanner that's been thrust into complicated electrical circuits. It's short-circuited everything.'

Cathy's heart had begun to thump painfully, though she scarcely knew why yet. She watched him with wide eyes, hardly breathing.

'But it seems likely that the actual circuits them-selves—the receptors in the brain—aren't permanently damaged. They simply can't communicate with each other while the scar tissue's there.'

'Fabian,' she whispered, 'you mean that they can cut away the scar——?'

'Actually, no.' He smiled gravely. 'When I said a spanner, I may have misled you. Perhaps I should have said like a big lump of molten solder that had fallen on to the wires and set there. It can't be cut away because it's organically fused with the brain itself. Cutting it would only cause more bleeding, more scar tissue. Possibly more damage, and possibly even total paralysis.'

'Oh.' Hope died in her, and she clung to his fingers with pain. 'I'm sorry, so sorry.'

'However,' he went on, 'the scar happens to be fairly hard. If it had been softer, the effect on my eyesight probably wouldn't have been nearly as bad—but the lesion is hard and brittle. Which means that although they can't operate in the conventional sense, they might be able to use ultrasound to make the situation a little better.'

'Ultrasound?' Her throat was dry and tight.

'A very high-pitched soundwave. They've used it successfully to break up kidney stones and certain kinds of tumour. They insert a kind of probe against the obstruction and the vibration literally disintegrates the material. Rather like Joshua and his trumpets outside the walls of Jericho.' He touched her cheek, unable to see her white face. 'You remember your Bible? Joshua ordered his men to blow their trumpets outside the walls of Jericho, and the stones just crumbled away.'

'I remember,' she whispered.

'Well, to get back to the twentieth century, while all this is going on, they insert a suction tube alongside the probe, and simply drain away the crumbled pieces. The whole thing can be done in an hour. Very good news for kidney stone patients.'

'And they want to operate on you?' she stammered.

'It's hardly an operation at all. They're simply going to cut a tiny hole through my temple—just here.' He touched her finger to a spot on his temple, just where the dark hair began to grow. 'They they insert this magic probe of theirs, along the curve of the brain, to the scar. And then Professor Sikorski blows his ultrasonic bugle—and with luck, the walls of this darkness come tumbling down.'

'Dear God!' She stared up at him with whirling hopes and fears in her heart. 'Will it work?'

'There are no guarantees,' he said with a shrug. And then for the first time ever, Cathy saw him give way to some of the feelings that must have been surging inside him since the accident. His fingers tightened around hers like steel, making her gasp, and a fierce intentness burned in his face. 'God in Heaven, Cathy—if they could do anything to lift this darkness—*anything*, even if it was no more than a glimpse of your sweet face—I'd go through any risks, any pain. I've got to take this offer, I can't refuse. Sikorski wasn't pulling any punches. He said there was a twenty-five per cent chance of some success. One per cent of total success.'

'Oh, Fabian——'

'But one per cent is a million times better than nothing. You don't know what this means to me, Cathy. I've been in such black despair, such torments. It's been like a wilderness, like being in exile. And now, at last, there's hope.'

'My darling,' she said with wet eyes, 'why don't you ever let me comfort you?'

'I told you that night,' he said, making a visible effort to control his emotions. 'I didn't want your pity, Cathy. And I don't want it now.'

'But Fabian,' she cried, 'I love you so much——'

His hand silenced her ruthlessly.

'Stop! No more of that, Cathy.' She tried to tear his hand away so that she could tell him what she felt, tell him what was in her heart, but he was as strong as steel. 'No more. For the love of God, if you want me to stay as I am and not turn into a child, don't say that again!'

He drew her against his chest. She could feel his heart pounding against her, a great engine that was running at full throttle now.

'Why?' she asked shakily.

'Because now is not the time,' he said, his own deep voice uneven. 'If the operation does anything for my sight——' He broke off, as though not trusting himself to speak. 'If and when there's any change in my condition, Cathy, I'll have so many things to say to you. Things which will change both our lives for ever.'

'Oh, say them now,' she begged.

'No.' His arms tightened around her fiercely. 'And there's something else. If this operation doesn't have any effect, I'm leaving London.'

'What?'

'Conrad Sikorski has told me about a school for the adult blind in New York. They have all the best techniques there. If I'm going to be blind for ever, then they can at least teach me how to cope. How to remain a lawyer. Maybe even how to remain a man.'

'I'll come with you,' she said urgently.

'No. If I go, I'll go alone.'

'No!'

'Yes,' he said quietly. 'Yes, Cathy. There's no other way. I could never inflict this on you for the rest of your life. It would be better for us to part.'

'Fabian,' she sobbed, 'I couldn't live without you——'

'And I couldn't live with you—not the way I am now. Seeing Sikorski has cleared up a lot of things for me, Cathy, shown me a lot of things. And one of them is that I couldn't stay with you any longer—not if I was still to be dependent on you for everything.'

'But we'd manage——'

'No. I could never be sure that what you felt was love, and not pity. Cathy, my sweet, I could live without your love—just. But I couldn't live with your pity.'

'I don't pity you,' she said desperately. 'If only you knew how I admire you, adore you——'

'Cathy.' His finger touched her trembling lips, silencing her. 'Cathy, I have to do this my way, or not at all. My feelings for you——' He smiled tautly. 'Well, my feelings for you are like a volcano, always ready to explode. But that explosion will never take place if I can't see you. If I don't know that I'm going to be your man—and not just your burden.'

'How can you say such things?'

'Because you're that sort of woman, Cathy.' His eyes were tender, wry. 'You love lame birds, strays, waifs—your work at the Addington proves that. Your heart is as wide as an ocean. And if you were honest with yourself, you yourself could never be sure that the feeling inside was really love, and not just—compassion.'

'I could be sure!' Her fingers dug into his shoulders. 'You know I could—you felt it yourself, when you made love to me!'

'I think you wanted me,' he smiled. The smile faded. 'But such passion isn't exactly a reliable guide. Perhaps you would want me still, for weeks, maybe months. But in a year? In three years? When the passion clears, what thoughts will be left, what pity? Pity turning to indifference, perhaps, to scorn and then to hatred.'

'No!'

'Who can say, Cathy? The human heart isn't predictable, like a machine.'

'But, Fabian——'

'Enough.' His smile was gone now. 'I'm going in to Guy's again tomorrow. They want to do more scans from different angles. And if everything's in order, Sikorski and another brain surgeon will probably operate in a very few days.'

'I see.' His face was as cool and as formal as it had been on the day she had first set eyes on him, across the expanse of his mahogany desk.

'And if the operation isn't successful——' He didn't complete the sentence. As he sensed the tears that were close behind Cathy's lids, his voice became gentler. 'And about what happened the other night—I needed you very badly, Cathy. I've never needed, or even wanted anyone so much in my life before. But I regret that now. It sounds hard, but I do. Making love forged a bond between us that will be very hard to break. And each time we make love again, that bond will be strengthened even more. And that,' he added gently, 'will only serve to confuse the issue very badly.'

'You think that what's between us can be just thrown away?' she asked bitterly.

'Not thrown away. It can be broken, though.'

'I'm glad you think so,' she said, pain and anger making her voice harsh. 'So we're never to make love again?'

'That would put unfair pressure on you to remain in a relationship that you may soon find intolerable,' he replied coolly, untouched by her passion.

'How can you be so calm and precise about this?' she demanded, close to hysteria. 'You talk about leaving me for ever as though it were just a stroll in the park to you——'

'Cathy——'

'—doesn't my love mean anything to you? Don't you give a damn whether I suffer or not? Or are you too afraid to accept my feelings?'

'This conversation stops right here,' Fabian said quietly, and there was a command in his face that silenced the agonised words that were rushing to her tongue, though it couldn't stop her tears. 'I'm sorry that my wishes seem unreasonable to you,' he went on in the same soft voice. 'And I'm sorry you think I don't care about you. I realise you want me to give you definite answers to all your questions, but I can't. We don't have much longer to wait, Cathy. Within a few days, we'll know what shape the rest of our lives are going to take.' He reached out to pat her cheek, his face staying as calm as though carved out of granite. 'Be patient. Be patient, and pray for me.'

Those words haunted Cathy for days. And the days themselves were haunting, a kind of limbo in which nothing was certain, nothing real. Patience, she discovered, soon wore thin. And prayers, in the end, were all she had left. Fabian had insisted that neither his own father nor hers should know anything of the planned operation. It would be too cruel, he had decided, to raise hope that might be bitterly crushed. The only person she could confide in was Kaspar, and Kaspar, with the fatalistic wisdom of ages, offered neither hope nor artificial optimism. 'What God wills,' he had said, stroking her cheek with wrinkled brown fingers, 'we must accept. It is our lot.'

Between Cathy and Fabian now a wall seemed to have arisen. There was a tension between them, an unspoken longing that showed itself only in a growing silence in both of them. She ached for him, yearned for him—yet from some deep well of inner strength, she was able to respect his wishes, and she did not try to touch him or give him the love her body longed to give. Nor did she make any further attempt to argue with him or change his will.

Instead, she vowed to herself that whatever the outcome of the operation, now scheduled for Friday morning, she would never leave Fabian. Could never leave him. If he intended to go to New York, she would follow, risking his fierce anger, perhaps even his hatred. She would follow him, if needs be, to the final limits of time and place.

Love, she had discovered, was a force more strange and powerful than she had ever dreamed. She had never believed in such things as fate or destiny. Her philosophy, if she had ever had one, had been that one got what one wanted, did what one needed to do. Yet now, looking back, it was impossible for her not to believe that some fate had chosen her out. Perhaps that feeling was because loving Fabian—and being desired, if not loved, in return—had made sense of the whole world for her. And when she considered the events that had led up to this time and place, she could see the thin line of destiny running through it all. The unhappy years with Timothy Coryat that had led up to the disaster of the *Caprice* pictures. And even before that, the loss of her mother which had impelled her into Tim's company, desperately seeking comfort.

And more than that, through all these strange events

ran the bright thread of love, unmistakable and vivid. The love she had yearned for, but had never known until Fabian. The love that had transformed her life, given it an importance, a meaning it had never had before.

Somehow, these thoughts helped her to accept Fabian's proud will. To the extent that when, early on Friday morning, she parted with him in the neurosurgery wing of the great hospital, she was able to fight back all tears, and all the useless, loving things she wanted to say.

And Fabian, with a cool self-control, played down any emotional aspect of the moment.

'I'll be conscious by two this afternoon,' he said calmly. 'If everything goes well, I should be allowed home by evening.'

'As easy as that?' she asked with a pale smile.

'According to Sikorski, this shouldn't be a lot worse than having a wisdom tooth out.'

'Good luck,' she said in a brittle voice. *Good luck*—of all the meaningless phrases. But he merely smiled.

'Thanks. Are you going into work this morning?'

'Kaspar's given me the day off.' Somehow, the conversation was unreal, something out of a play. 'I thought I'd do some shopping.'

'Good.' Cathy stared at him in silence, aching inside.

And then Conrad Sikorski had arrived, his bearded and grizzled face smiling, accompanied by the second surgeon, and with a passionate, brief kiss on his lips, she had fled down the tiled corridors, her heart too full for tears or prayers.

Ten days later, Kaspar Aprahamian came down from the upper level of the shop to where Cathy was studying the exquisite golds and reds of a silk rug.

'You have a visitor,' he announced.

'A man?'

'A woman.' Kaspar smiled, his face breaking into a thousand wrinkles. 'Very glamorous. Go upstairs—you can talk in peace there. I will bring tea in a little while.'

'Thanks, Kaspar.' Slightly puzzled, Cathy ran up the stairs to the showroom—and stopped dead with an unpleasant jolt. The visitor wasn't a client, but Cerise Hunniford, today playing the black widow in a jet-coloured Thai silk ensemble that set her flame-red hair and blue eyes off to glittering perfection.

'The delectable Miss Milner,' she purred. 'What a charming little shop you work in! Who was that wizened little *gnome* I've just been speaking to?'

'Kaspar is one of the world's greatest authorities on Oriental carpets. As you well know.' Cathy came slowly forward. 'What can I do for you, Cerise?'

'Just conversation. Information.' Cerise settled herself on an ottoman, her smile fixed, but her eyes merciless.

'I'm busy right now,' Cathy said coldly. 'What is it you want to know?'

'Short and to the point.' Cerise lit a gold-tipped cigarette and exhaled smoke luxuriously. Her lips, Cathy noticed, were red as blood. 'I understand that Fabian Blackthorne went into Guy's Hospital last week, for an operation.'

Cathy sat down slowly, her eyes never leaving Cerise's face. 'That's right,' she said impassively.

'And this operation was aimed at restoring his eyesight?'

'Yes.'

Cerise's smile tightened. 'So it *is* true! You've managed to keep the whole thing quite a little secret, haven't you?'

'Not even Fabian's father knew that the operation was going to take place,' Cathy said quietly. 'He didn't want anyone's expectations to be raised.'

'Except yours.' Cerise blew smoke in Cathy's direction. 'You've become Fabian's guardian, haven't you, my dear? Quite the trusted confidante!'

'The operation was unsuccessful.' Cathy drew in a slow breath. Even now, the memory of that bitter disappointment jerked at her heartstrings. The wave of sickness that had overcome her that afternoon at Guy's had been one of the most horrible blows she had ever received. 'They were using a new technique,' she went on, watched by Cerise's intent eyes. 'They tried to remove the scar tissue that was pressing on the sight centre, but they didn't manage.'

'He's still blind?'

'Yes.' And even though the blow to Fabian must have been even greater than to her, he had found the strength to comfort her, to wipe away her tears. Cerise Hunniford's face softened momentarily, revealing an unexpected vulnerability behind the ruthless façade.

'Poor Fabian,' she whispered. 'Then there's no hope?'

For a few seconds Cathy struggled with herself; perhaps if she hadn't seen that softness, that tenderness in Cerise's face a moment ago, she might have kept the news to herself. But now she couldn't refuse Cerise the information.

'They're going to try again, tomorrow morning.'

The hard look flashed back into Cerise's eyes.

'What do you mean?'

'The probe they used on the first operation was the wrong size.' Cathy sighed, nerves fluttering in her heart as she thought of how much depended on tomorrow's operation. 'I don't understand the technicalities of it. But they removed the biggest obstacles last week, even though the surgery didn't affect Fabian's sight. Tomorrow they're going to use a fine probe to try and remove the last particles of the scar tissue. Those are the fragments that are lodged in the sight centre itself.' Cerise's face was frozen, her motionless cigarette sending a thin column of smoke into the still air. Below, Kaspar could be heard rattling teacups.

'Well?' Cerise whispered.

'They have more confidence this time.' The words came unwillingly to Cathy's lips, as though saying them might bring bad luck to dash the cup of hope away from her. 'They say they could well succeed this time.'

'Who's *they*?'

'Conrad Sikorski and his team. He's a great psychotherapist and neuro-surgeon—blindness is his speciality.' She thought of Sikorski's grizzled face, the

wise, tired eyes, the wonderful smile. 'He—he thinks
he'll be able to restore Fabian's sight this time.' Cathy
looked away from Cerise, at the wonderful colours of
the rugs spread all around the shop. Cerise exhaled her
breath in a sharp laugh.

'That's more like it,' she said grimly. 'That's what I
came here to hear.' Kaspar came up the stairs with tea
and delicate squares of Turkish Delight. When he had
retired below again, Cerise stirred her tea with a cold
smile.

'I'm so pleased to hear all this, my dear Catherine.
Not only because I'm happy for Fabian Blackthorne—
but because, you see, this news means that Fabian and I
will soon be together again.'

'I thought you'd resigned all claims over Fabian,'
Cathy said, drily amused by Cerise's self-confidence.

'Oh, I had—I had indeed. I told you, sweetie, I'm no
damn good with lame ducks. Loonies and blind people
just give me the *shivers*! But now that Fabian's going to
see again——' She smiled over her teacup, her eyes
brilliant with triumph. Cathy leaned back in her couch,
crossing her ankles.

'Supposing Fabian doesn't want you back?' Cathy
asked calmly. 'Supposing he wants me?'

'A minor obstacle. Because you'll politely step out of
the picture, won't you?'

'You're very confident,' Cathy remarked with a faint
smile. 'But I happen to love Fabian.'

'Love?' A spasm crossed the beautiful face. 'Oh, no
doubt he's become dependent on you. You saw to that,
didn't you? You took advantage of his blindness to
make sure that he needed you.'

For the first time, a red glow of anger appeared in
Cathy's cheeks, but she remained calm.

'And I'm just going to disappear now, am I?'

'That's right.'

'Where, may I ask?'

'I thought America would do.'

'You're joking!' Cathy set down her teacup,
beginning to feel that Cerise's mind must be going.

'What on earth is going to induce me to go to America?'

'These.' Something dropped on to the table in front of Cathy, and her hand moved automatically to pick it up.

And then the shock hit her, as though a poisonous snake had suddenly reared in front of her. Cerise Hunniford drew deeply on her cigarette, and exhaled with a thin smile of pleasure.

'It does me good to see you put on that innocent virgin act, my dear—you're *so* good at it. But now you do see why you're going to America. Don't you?'

Cathy lifted the top photograph. It showed a naked woman pulling the brim of a red staw hat down over a provocative smile. Her full, uptilted breasts teased the viewer. In the next, the woman was standing at a window, undoing the knot of her raven hair. The soft mist didn't obscure the elgance of her slim figure.

Cathy Milner's figure. Cathy Milner's face.

CHAPTER NINE

CATHY looked back into Cerise's mocking blue eyes.

'Where did these come from?'

Cerise was genuinely, unaffectedly amused. She leaned back to laugh heartily. 'Poor little Miss Milner— what a child you are!'

'You said you'd given all the pictures to Fabian,' Cathy said numbly. 'You said they were all there. I burned them all——'

'You're an unending source of amusement to me, Cathy. Did you really think I wouldn't keep one or two behind? No, of course not. You didn't have the brains to realise that I wanted Fabian, and could see how besotted you were with him.' She lit another cigarette, enjoying Cathy's dazed horror. 'I had copies of the best negatives made—it's a simple photographic process.' Fresh laughter shook Cerise. 'Don't you find this at *all* amusing?'

'No.' Cathy pushed the pile of photographs away from her. Six weeks ago, the sight of them would have shattered her. Now she simply waited, taut with anger, to hear what Cerise had to say.

'What are you going to do with those pictures?' she asked quietly.

'Oh, I'm going to print them,' said Cerise, as though surprised by the question. 'They're coming out next month. The best one's going on the cover, actually. Isn't that an honour? Yes, we feel that the impact will do *wonders* for your public image.'

'Fabian obtained an injunction to stop you printing anything about me for three months,' Cathy said calmly. 'You'll be breaking the terms of that injunction.'

'Oh, I'm going to, no question about it, sweetie. I'm not afraid of a fine—or even the confiscation of a few hundred thousand copies. Even if only a few thousand more get on to the shelves, the damage will be done. In fact,' she smiled, sipping tea as calmly as though she were a suburban matron discussing a church fête, 'even if you stop me from distributing altogether, the publicity will be quite terrific. Why, you'll get fan-mail! Won't Fabian be pleased to see the woman he adores becoming so popular?'

'You're mad, Cerise,' said Cathy, but her hands were shaking.

'And I'm sure your father will be over the moon. How is his health lately, by the way? His heart's much stronger now, so I hear. I do hope all the excitement of your success won't put any *strain* on him.'

'Can I cut this short?' Cathy said icily. 'I don't find your line of repartee either intimidating or amusing.' Ignoring the furious expression on Cerise's face, she went on, 'I take it you now expect me to turn tail and run for America?'

'Just for a long holiday—say, six months. No emotional scenes, please. No forwarding address, no letters, no attempt to contact Fabian. You'll just go, without telling anybody. I'll do the rest. A note, perhaps—something about finding someone else.'

'And you think he'll believe that?' asked Cathy, watching Cerise's tanned face.

'Time will convince him. You'll be gone—and he won't ever hear from you. He'll have to believe it, won't he? And if you ever *do* contact him,' Cerise smiled harshly, 'I'll see that those pictures are printed immediately.'

'I see,' said Cathy. She felt oddly calm. It was as though some nightmare had returned in daylight, trying to frighten her. Except that she was no longer frightened. Not the way she had been, anyway. She'd grown up since then.

'You've wasted your time, Cerise,' she said quietly.

Cerise's eyes widened in disbelief. 'Don't be such a damned fool!' she snapped in a brittle voice. 'You're just a child, Cathy. What the hell can you know about love?' She dragged at her cigarette, her blue eyes narrowed in an unseeing stare. 'You've barely had time to find out what life's all about!'

'I love Fabian,' said Cathy in the same quiet voice. 'And what's more important, from your point of view, is that he doesn't love you.'

'Leave that to me,' Cerise said with a hard smile. 'If there's one thing I've learned in life, it's how to please a man.' She ground her cigarette out. 'Believe me, I'll make him love me.' She took up the scattered photographs, and thrust them at Cathy. 'Look at them! Think of them, in every newsagent in the country. You couldn't face it, Cathy. You haven't the guts—and nor has your sick father. You'd better start arranging that trip to America, sweetie—you don't have much time.'

'I've got all the time in the world.' Suddenly, a great calm had settled on Cathy. She had faced her nightmare, and felt deep inside that she was strong enough to fight it. 'I ought to hate you, I suppose, but I can't, because I know that you care for Fabian. But I'm not going. My place is at Fabian's side.' She gave the pictures back to Cerise, and rose. Her eyes were steady as she looked into the glittering blue eyes. 'Why not take that American trip yourself, Cerise?'

Disbelief had drawn the colour out of Cerise's cheeks. She whispered an obscenity, and rose to face Cathy.

'You're saying you'll take me on?'

'Take you on?' Cathy smiled gently. 'You don't figure all that large in my thoughts, Cerise. Fabian is the most important thing in my life. He always will be. And nothing you or anybody else does to me can ever change that. I'm saying that I'll never leave him—until he asks me to.'

'Wait and see about *that*!' hissed Cerise, really furious now. 'By God, you little——'

'And if you think you can make a man like Fabian Blackthorne love you, you know less about human nature than you imagine,' Cathy cut through the insult. 'For your own sake, face reality. You're in for a very painful revelation some day if you don't.'

'When I want your advice,' Cerise snarled, 'I'll pull the bloody chain!' She pointed a quivering forefinger at Cathy's face. 'Get going, Cathy,' she said harshly. 'And don't come back. Because if you don't, your body will be on show the length and breadth of England!' She pulled the door open, letting the busy noise of a sunny Bond Street morning into the quiet shop. 'I mean that, girl.'

'I believe you,' Cathy said softly. 'Goodbye, Cerise.'

Cerise Hunniford's face was ugly with anger as she slammed the door shut behind her and stalked down the street.

Kaspar came anxiously up the stairs to find Cathy.

'Is everything all right?' he queried.

She thrust her hands deep into the pockets of her jacket.

'Yes,' she said quietly, 'everything's fine, Kaspar.'

'What did that woman want?'

'To threaten me.' She smiled rather tiredly at Kaspar's expression of shock. Cerise had meant her threat, she knew that. She was quite capable of defying an injunction to try and injure Cathy, maybe even risking her whole business—for the sake of Fabian Blackthorne.

'You want me to call the police?' Kaspar asked anxiously.

'No, that isn't necessary.'

'Then what will you do?' he asked. 'Could she hurt you?'

'I don't know.' She had a sudden vision of Fabian under the surgeon's probe. 'I can't even think about it yet, Kaspar—there are too many other things on my mind. I'll cross that stile when I come to it.'

She took the old man's arm, and they walked down the stairs again.

Cerise would do it, though. Of that, Cathy was utterly certain.

Wednesday.

She sat in the day-room, taut with anxiety, her mind

completely unable to focus on the magazine she was
holding. Months ago she had sat in this very room,
waiting to hear whether Fabian Blackthorne was to live
or die. The outcome today was no less important—for
both of them.

Even the sword that Cerise Hunniford had suspended
over her head was forgotten now. Her mind was in the
operating theatre, with the ultra-sophisticated equip-
ment, the dedicated team, the man who lay under the
lights.

The hand of the electric clock on the wall crept by,
round and round, a slow and remorseless pace that was
beginning to tell on Cathy's nerves. Again, Fabian had
insisted that no one else know that the operation was
under way.

Which also meant that Cathy was utterly alone in her
anxiety. She could confide only in Kaspar, who had
given her the day off again. Please, she prayed to
whatever god or gods might be listening to her lone
voice, please let him see. Take whatever you want from
me—but let him see.

It was as she was looking up helplessly at the clock
for the thousandth time that the doors swung open, and
Conrad Sikorski came into the day-room, his bearded
face wreathed in a smile that consisted of a hundred
tiny wrinkles.

She rose on unsteady legs.

'Ah, Cathy. He's conscious. Would you like to see
him?'

      'Has——' She had to try again. 'Has the operation
succeeded?'

'Come and see for yourself.' His big hand, so broad
and earthy-looking to be a surgeon's, took her elbow
gently, and he led her through the ward to a curtained-
off room at the end. In the dim light, Fabian was lying
propped up against the pillows.

And as Conrad Sikorski let her walk slowly inside,
Fabian's head turned to her, the grey eyes meeting hers.
A slow smile curved across the passionate mouth.

Her own eyes so blurred that she could hardly find

her way to him, Cathy went forward. His hands took hers, guiding her to his chest, where she lay cradled in his arms, too full for words.

'My Cathy,' he murmured, stroking her hair, 'I'd forgotten how beautiful you are. So very beautiful.' They lay in silence, locked together in the soft light.

From the door, Conrad Sikorski's deep voice came quietly.

'He's going to be a bit dazed for the rest of the day. Nothing serious, just the after-affects of the local anaesthetic, more than anything else. But he can go home the day after tomorrow if he wants to. Can you manage to look after him again?'

Cathy raised her head slowly, her smiled dazed.

'I—I think so.'

'Of course she can,' said Fabian in the same dreamy voice. 'She's going to look after me for the rest of my life . . .'

'Good,' the neuro-surgeon smiled. 'It might be best to let him sleep for an hour or two now. How d'you feel, Mr Blackthorne?'

'Rotten,' Fabian admitted, his mouth wry. 'And the light hurts like sin.'

'That'll pass.' He glanced at Cathy. 'Happy?' he smiled.

'It's a miracle,' she said unevenly. 'I don't think we're ever going to be able to thank you——'

'All this gratitude,' the surgeon protested. 'But it was very satisfactory, I must say.' He grinned his wrinkled grin. 'The scar is quite gone, almost as though it had never existed. Mr Blackthorne's sight seems to be perfect. Of course,' he added, 'there may be headaches for a day or two. We had to drill a small hole in his skull, and the probe's been in twice now. But yes, the operation was most satisfactory.'

'He's a genius,' Fabian said sleepily. 'Pure genius.'

'Of course. Cathy, can I leave it to you to break the news to his father?'

'I'll do it in a few moments,' Cathy promised. Her heart was full, brimming over. There's enough happiness here, she thought dimly, to last both of us the rest of our lives. The surgeon looked at Cathy, who was gazing into Fabian's face with an expression he had seldom seen on any woman's face, and smiled to himself again. Without further speech, he let the door of the ward close silently, and walked briskly to the charge office.

'Sister?' they heard him call. 'Mr Blackthorne's going home on Friday—around six, probably.'

Inside the dimly-lit room, Fabian was drawing a wandering finger down the line of Cathy's face. His eyes, cloudy and half open, were drinking in her rather shaky smile.

'I've dreamed of this face for so long,' he said tenderly. 'Now I hardly know whether I'm seeing it—or still dreaming.'

'This is no dream, my love.' Her lips clung to him in a kiss that was as passionate as she dared. 'And you've got the rest of your life to see in. For now, just close your eyes and dream an hour or two longer.'

'Tyrant,' he smiled, but obediently let his long lashes droop over the cloudy grey eyes. 'I'm too tired to tell you what I feel, Cathy. Too tired and too headachy to be able to express the inexpressible.' He smiled, his fingers tightening over her own. 'Maybe tomorrow . . .' His voice trailed off into silence.

She sat by his side, watching him with wonder, her heart singing a paean of thankfulness.

'Sleep, beloved,' she whispered. 'Sleep now.'

And when she was sure he was asleep, she slipped quietly out of the room to find Conrad Sikorski. There was a great deal she wanted to say to him.

She found him in the canteen, sitting with Andrea Lorenz, who had arrived in the meantime. The psychiatrist rose to greet her with a hug, sharing her joy.

'How is he?' asked Conrad Sikorski, ushering a rather trembly Cathy to the seat next to him.

'Asleep,' she said. 'Professor Sikorski, he's a very special man. By giving him sight, you've given life to so many other people, too. I know that any words are going to be inadequate to thank you for what you've done, but I just want you to know——'

'No thanks are necessary,' he said gently as he saw the wetness on her lids. 'No thanks at all. I'm as delighted as you that the operation went well. Just look after him now.'

'Here.' Andrea practical as ever, had brought a cup of pink canteen tea, and Cathy gulped at it gratefully. Andrea's brown eyes were tender as she sat down opposite Cathy. 'There's nothing to stand in the way of your happiness now, is there?'

The thought of Cerise Hunniford's threat crossed Cathy's mind like a shadow crossing sunlit water. Then she thrust the thought aside. Not today. I'll think about that later, not now. Now is a time for joy.

'Nothing,' she said softly. 'Nothing at all.'

'I suppose you won't have time for Ursula this weekend, now that Fabian's going to be recovering. I'll cancel the visit——'

'No,' Cathy smiled. 'No, I want Ursie to share all this, Andrea. Especially now that Fabian can see her and play with her. I've got so much joy that there's plenty to spare.'

'Good,' beamed Andrea. 'You can pick her up any time you like.' She turned to the surgeon, and explained briefly about Ursula's visit. 'Conrad mightn't have been so keen to see Fabian if I hadn't told him about your work at the Addington,' she concluded. 'Funny how life works out, isn't it?'

'Very funny,' Cathy agreed gently.

'And now—Conrad was just giving me a blow-by-blow account of the operation.' She turned to the smiling surgeon. 'Would you mind starting from the beginning again—for Cathy's benefit?'

The weekend was glorious in every way. It was a time of joy after long darkness—and Ursula was perhaps the most spontaneous of all, sharing their delight with unaffected enthusiasm, even though she had little idea of what the party was about.

Keith Blackthorne and Cedric Milner, both still dazed
by the news, had been sitting in the garden with Fabian
all Saturday morning. Even the day seemed to echo
their celebration, the sunlight pouring down so
brilliantly that Fabian was forced to don dark glasses to
protect his still sensitive eyes. The blue sky, cloudless
and serene, seemed to promise a future unshadowed
and joyous.

The grim inner realisation that she now had to face
Cerise Hunniford's threat had awoken with Cathy that
morning, long before she had driven to the Addington
to pick up Ursula. Yes, she had defied Cerise, and knew
she was never going to give in to what Cerise wanted
her to do. But she couldn't help being afraid of the
consequences—not so much to herself as to her father.
The fear nagged at her, gnawing her happiness. She
fought it down as best she could, but it wouldn't quite
go away. She was going to have to face it somehow.
And somehow, she was going to tell her father
everything. She'd wanted to wait a long time before
revealing what a fool she had been, but now . . .

In the general joy, she had scarcely had a minute
alone with Fabian. Their eyes had met, their glances
containing such intense feeling that Cathy's heart had
lurched inside her every time he had looked at her; but
almost deliberately she had avoided being alone with
him. Their time was yet to come.

She had been throwing the ball for Ursie's clumsy
hands to catch.

'Let's stop now,' she said, taking the child's hands
and spinning her in a shrieking circle. 'Cathy's
exhausted.'

'Later, then?' Ursula made her promise.

'Later.'

'And will Fabian play too?'

'Sure. Now, you go and explore the garden while I
get my breath back.' Cathy watched the pigtailed figure
scamper off into the drowsy garden, and then turned to
glance at the umbrella-shaded table where the two
fathers and Fabian were reclining. There was a burst of

masculine laughter at something Fabian had said—laughter she hadn't heard for weeks.

'Come on,' called Fabian, waving to her, 'come and join us!'

Catching the lump in her throat, she walked over to them. His eyes were bright as he took off his sunglasses to watch her.

'You look lovely,' he said, with a smile that jolted her square in the solar plexus. 'A personification of summer.'

'Fabian was telling us about the operation,' Keith Blackthorne said. The tired look on his face had faded now, and some of his old vigour had returned. 'How you two managed to keep the whole affair a secret is beyond me.'

'It wasn't very nice,' Sir Cedric agreed gravely. 'We're not children, you know.'

'Of course not,' Fabian agreed solemnly, and the two old men smiled in unison.

'Well,' Keith said with a sigh, 'perhaps it was the best way, after all. There's a poem that begins, "Surprised by joy". That's how we felt last night—surprised by joy.' He laid his hand on his son's shoulder quietly. 'I'm so glad for you, my boy, so very glad.'

In the silence that followed, the distant chime of the doorbell floated to them from the house.

'I'll go,' volunteered Sir Cedric, but Cathy, stood up. 'You relax. It'll probably be the milkman.'

Fabian's smiled followed her as she walked to the house. Yes, she thought, we have so much to be thankful for, so much to praise God for . . . She walked through the house and opened the door.

Not the milkman.

Cerise Hunniford, her blue eyes meeting Cathy's with a hard challenge.

'I heard the good news last night,' she said coolly. 'May I come in?'

'What do you want?' Cathy asked quietly.

'To see Fabian.' Cerise brushed an invisible speck of dust off her lapel, and smiled brightly. 'I think he and I should go out and celebrate tonight.'

The insolence took Cathy's breath away for a second.

'Cerise,' she said, trying to keep her temper, 'you just abandoned him when he was blind. Don't you think he's seen through you long ago?'

'There's more between Fabian and me than you'll ever know,' snapped Cerise. 'I trust you've had second thoughts about your foolish bravado of the other day. I mean to do what I threatened, Cathy.'

'I'm sure you do,' Cathy said softly. 'But if you're wrong about Fabian? If he doesn't want you?'

'In that case,' Cerise grated, her mouth ugly, 'I'll print those pictures anyway. I'm the original dog in the manger, sweetheart. If I can't have him, I'll make damned sure you pay for it.' She smiled harshly. 'I've even got a selection in my handbag. I thought your father might like to see them. Now, it's very rude to keep guests waiting on your doorstep. And I can't wait to see Fabian. So can I come in now?'

Cathy stood rigid at the door, struggling with a frightening urge to snatch up one of the bronze figurines on the sideboard and smash Cerise down with it . . .

And then a little figure in pigtails was at her side, tugging at her dress.

'Cathy, Cathy,' called Ursula, 'let's play some more!'

To Cathy's astonishment, Cerise Hunniford shrank back as though she had been confronted by a ghost. Her blue eyes were wide, her thin lips suddenly bloodless.

And a no less amazing change had come over Ursula. Her almond eyes focused in bewilderment on Cerise, and she took a tentative step forward, stretching out her hand.

'Mummy?'

Cerise was frozen, unable to move. The child came forward, peering up into the white face under the flame-red hair.

'Mummy? It is you? It is!' She ran forward, clinging to Cerise's fine silk skirt with eager fingers. 'Mummy, it's been so long! Why didn't you ever come to see me?'

Cerise turned to face Cathy's amazed expression.

'What have you done?' she whispered savagely. 'You little bitch, what trick is this?'

'There's no trick,' Cathy stammered in bewilderment.

'Then what's my daughter doing here?'

Understanding dawned on Cathy. Not by degrees, but all at once, as though she'd known the whole story all along. Suddenly, it all fitted, everything—all she knew of Ursula's background, Cerise Hunniford's horror of people with disabilities—everything meshed now.

And now, as she stared into Cerise's stricken face, Cathy knew what it was that had made Cerise Hunniford cynical and worldly-wise. What had driven her into a career based in the callous exploitation of other people's weaknesses.

'You even forgot my birthday,' Ursula said reproachfully, moved by some flash of memory.

Cerise stared down at her, then up at Cathy.

'What is she doing here?' she repeated in the same whisper.

'She's come to spend the weekend with me.' Cathy walked forward slowly, and stroked Ursula's puzzled, upturned face, her eyes never leaving Cerise's. 'Believe me, Cerise, I had no idea at all. I wouldn't engineer something like this. Ursie just happens to be a special friend.'

'Cathy's my best friend,' Ursula carolled.

'I don't understand.' Abruptly, like a marionette whose strings had been slashed, Cerise seemed to crumple. Cathy led her inside, and guided her to a sofa. 'I don't understand at all,' Cerise repeated dazedly.

'I've been working at the Addington hospital for the past three years or more,' Cathy explained slowly. 'Three times a week. I do remedial work there. This weekend, they happened to let Ursula come home with me, that's all.'

'Cathy loves me,' said Ursula with a child's confidence. She scrambled up into Cerise's lap, oblivious to her mother's numb expression. Now that

Cerise was here, Ursula had accepted her presence with the readiness of complete innocence. Cathy had noticed the same easy acceptance of things in other mentally handicapped children. 'Mummy, is Cathy my real mummy?'

'Your real mummy?' With strange slowness, Cerise turned to look into the almond eyes.

'We had fish last night, and potatoes, and peas and beans.' Inventing freely, Ursula rambled on in the tense silence. 'And jelly and custard, and rice, and rice pudding——'

'I'm so sorry,' said Cathy, feeling a real pang of pity at Cerise's total shock.

'Cathy comes to visit me,' Ursula volunteered reproachfully. 'She shows me how to paint. And she brings me toys. She says I mustn't be afraid of the dark. And,' she added with a burst of delight, 'I'm sleeping here tonight!'

'I'm your real mummy,' whispered Cerise, her trembling hand brushing the child's tangled hair back from her eyes. 'You damn well remember that. *I'm* your real mummy.'

'I know,' Ursula answered with a touch of impatience. 'Can we go and play now?'

'I tried—I swear I tried.' Cerise was talking to Cathy now, who was sitting silently beside her. 'I tried for almost a year, but I couldn't stand it—I might have done something terrible——'

'I understand,' Cathy said gently.

'I'm no damned good with lame ducks. I have enough to do looking after myself.' Cerise rocked the puzzled child fretfully in her arms. 'But I do love her—I always have, I always will.'

'I didn't even know you'd been married.'

'It only lasted a year. And when Ursula was born, the bastard left for Australia.' Cerise let the child slip off her lap, and tugged her dress straight with automatic fingers. Her eyes looked swollen. Without looking at Cathy, she asked, 'What sort of work do you do with Ursula?'

Cathy explained as briefly as she could, trying to give Cerise some idea of what her work meant. It was hard to imagine Cerise as a mother, harder still to understand the terrible vulnerability she had just seen in those blue eyes.

Cerise was silent until Cathy had finished.

'If I had the strength, I'd look after her myself. But I haven't. And she's left in the hands of people like you.'

'It's better that way,' Cathy said calmly. 'I don't know how I'd feel if my daughter turned out like Ursie——'

'Oh, you'd cope.' Cerise's smile was bittersweet. 'You're different, Cathy Milner. Not like me.' She drew Ursula closer, turning to her.

'You like Cathy?'

'Yes. Are you staying to play?'

'Not today. Maybe some other time. Is she good to you?'

'She's my best friend,' Ursula repeated simply. 'She's even in my dreams.'

'She's even in your dreams.' Cerise's slender features were wry. 'I suppose you think Mummy ought to give all her happiness to your Cathy?'

Ursula was silent, not understanding.

'Life's very strange,' Cerise sighed dreamily. 'So very strange. I came here to demolish you, Cathy. Now you've demolished me.' She watched as Ursula wandered across the room, her concentration span now exhausted. 'Very strange.'

'I'm sorry, Cerise.'

'Are you?' She glanced at Cathy with a tired smile. 'Yes. Yes, I believe you are.' She rose abruptly and walked to the mirror on the wall to straighten her make-up. 'His vision's perfect?' she asked, her mouth stretched as she applied lipstick.

'Yes.' Cerise's eyes caught hers in the mirror.

'Bitch,' she said with the same wry smile. 'If I didn't hate you so much, I'd wish you happiness.' She dropped the lipstick into her bag and shut it with a decisive click. 'I don't think I'll be seeing Fabian after all. I've just remembered an important date with my Iraqui gazelle.' She turned to Ursula. 'Goodbye, darling. Come and give Mummy a kiss.'

Cathy walked her out, feeling that it really was all over now. At the door, Cerise turned and studied the green eyes, the cloud of raven hair, the perfect oval face. 'Yes,' she said drily, 'you're beautiful. Pity—*Caprice* would have made a mint out of that face and body.'

'You're not going to print those pictures?' Cathy asked quietly.

'No. No, this time they're really going into the fire. And maybe it'll be me on that flight to New York after all.' Cerise patted Cathy's cheek briefly. 'Have fun. And don't steal my daughter as well as my man.' Her high heels click-clicked down the path, and she didn't look back as she stepped into the red Porsche on the drive, not even when Ursula called goodbye after her.

Cathy, holding Ursula's hand, watched the car turn the lane and disappear for ever. Then she closed the door, and Ursula ran unconcernedly out into the back garden. By rights, Cathy should have been triumphing now. Instead, her deep, quiet gladness was touched with sympathy for a woman whom life had treated harshly, and who had responded harshly in turn . . .

She turned as Fabian opened the door softly, and met the deep grey eyes that seemed to look into her very soul, and as always, felt that electric shock to the heart that she knew would never fade.

'You're so lovely.' He took her face in his hands, his expression wondering. 'Sometimes I feel that this is the only reason I was given back these eyes—just to be able to see your lovely face.' He kissed her gently, feeling the first shudder of her response before drawing back.

'Did you hear any of that?' she asked in a whisper.

'Most of it. I'm afraid being blind has made my hearing sharper than it should be.' He smiled slightly. 'Besides, I was in the next room. I take it Cerise was threatening to publish some shots she'd held back if you didn't disappear and leave the field clear for her?'

'Something like that,' Cathy nodded ruefully.

'Why didn't you tell me?' He touched her lips with a reproving finger.

'It was my personal little nightmare,' she said, closing her eyes. 'And I didn't know whether you mightn't still want Cerise after all . . .'

'Don't you know yet?' he smiled, drawing her closer.

'She's so sophisticated, so sexy——'

'And you don't think you might be all of those things?'

'I don't know,' she said in confusion, her mind blurred, as always, by his closeness. 'I thought you liked her.'

'I did.' His grin was wicked. 'I thought Cerise was a bit of hot stuff when I first met her.'

'Oh,' Cathy said miserably.

'You wouldn't want me to lie to you, would you?' he said gravely. But there was a smile in his eyes. 'Oh, Cathy, I never felt anything for Cerise. Silly girl! How could I? That first time I kissed you, my whole world seemed to turn inside out. I'd never known anything like it.'

'Are you teasing me?' she asked uncomfortably.

'No, I'm not teasing you.' His mouth affirmed the truth of that against hers, a velvety caress that set her pulses fluttering. 'You see? No one else can do that to you. And no one else will ever do this to me.' He took her hand and laid it over his heart. The beat was hard and fast under her fingers.

'Oh, Fabian——'

'My interest in Cerise died a very long time ago, Cathy.' He brushed the dark cloud of hair away from her brow. 'And she sensed that immediately. That was what made her so vindictive—the knowledge that I was falling in love with you.'

She clung to him, unable to speak.

'I've loved you for weeks, Cathy. I don't know how you could have thought otherwise. It seemed so glaringly obvious to me—and yet you never seemed to realise . . .'

'You were so harsh, so cruel,' she stammered, joy and tears tumbling together in her heart. 'You—you seemed so upset when Cerise dropped you after the accident——'

'Yes, I was upset. That hit me very hard, Cathy—but not for the reasons you thought. Because I was terrified you might be feeling the same revulsion—that only your sweet nature might be stopping you from showing it, and walking away as Cerise did.'

'How could you have felt that?' she asked in shaky wonder. 'When you said you'd be going to America alone, I nearly died!'

'Wild words,' Fabian smiled ruefully. 'I should have admitted to myself that I wasn't going anywhere without you, ever. But I was so desperate, my sweet, so afraid . . . Maybe even a little crazy.'

He led her to the window, and together they looked out over the sunlit garden where Ursula played, and their fathers sat talking, figures made small by distance, perspective, and age.

'Life is full of ironies, isn't it, my sweet?' He drew her close. 'It wasn't until I lost my sight that I learned how to see. To see spiritually, I mean. Before the accident, you'd been exciting, intriguing. But after it, you became all in all to me. Because it was in those first days of blindness, when my mind had so many other things to deal with—shock, rage, horror—that I discovered what you meant to me. How haunted I was by your voice, your face. How your gentle ways had soaked into me, wrapped themselves around the very roots of my being.'

'My love,' she shuddered, half in a dream, 'I didn't dare imagine . . .'

'I can't think why,' he smiled. 'But the irony didn't end there. Because at the very point I'd discovered how much I needed you, I'd lost you for ever.'

'Because of your blindness?' He nodded. 'Oh, Fabian, how in heaven's name could you have been so stubborn, so mad? Didn't you know that I'd have loved you for ever, no matter what? In all that brilliant brain of yours, wasn't there even an inkling of the way I felt?'

'I wanted you too much,' he said simply. 'You were too important to me for me to afford the slightest doubt. And it wasn't just that I was maddened by my blindness. For one thing, we scarcely knew each other. Not nearly as well, anyway, as most couples do who are contemplating marriage.' Cathy looked up at him in disbelief, and he smiled quietly, his mouth passionate. 'We *are* contemplating marriage, aren't we?'

'I——' The words stuck in her throat, and her jade-green eyes were misty. 'Nothing else is real to me, darling,' she whispered huskily. 'Nothing but you.'

'In which case,' he said softly, the bite of his fingers into her arms betraying his emotion, 'I want you to be my wife, Cathy. If I didn't want a big white wedding, I'd say tomorrow. Will next month do?'

Her lips gave him her answer, a kiss that was both exquisite surrender and delicious possession. Not even in her sweetest dreams had she allowed her imagination to come this far. Yet now, as she melted in his arms, tasting his desire, his power, she knew that there was nothing else in the world for her. Nothing but marriage to Fabian, their shared life together, the conception of his children, deep in her womb . . .

Ages passed, and then she lay against his chest with wildly beating heart, her long lashes shut.

'There are certain conditions, Cathy.' She looked up at him. 'One of them,' he said gently, 'is that you start taking yourself more seriously. And by that I mean enrolling at university for a course in child psychology. You've got much too great a talent not to train it. Will you promise me that?'

'Yes,' she nodded, 'I promise, Fabian.'

'Excellent. Andrea Lorenz is already working on the details—she seems to feel that you have a good chance of getting into L.S.E. in the autumn.'

'You've been conspiring,' she accused, wide-eyed. 'Behind my back!'

'I admit the charge. You've been ever so slightly off the rails since your mother left, my sweet. Now that you're firmly back on them again, I think I can safely give you a little push in the right direction!'

'Oh, my love,' sighed Cathy, 'and I thought you were indifferent to me!'

'That was my cunning,' Fabian said ruefully. 'Yes, I was cruel to you. I was only hoping to get under that calm exterior of yours. I needed to find out what you were really like, whether you were as gentle and sweet as you seemed, or whether I'd been fooling myself.' He smiled wryly. 'I hoped that if I aroused your passions, your inner truth would come out. All I seemed to do was drive myself crazy with frustrated desire.'

'To say nothing of what you did to me,' she smiled tenderly.

'I don't think I've ever been in such turmoil . . .' She luxuriated in the power of his arms, smiling up at him.

'But will you think me as sexy as slinky Cerise, with her black outfits and six-inch heels?'

'You're the only woman I've ever wanted,' said Fabian, his eyes devouring her hungrily. 'No one else has ever come close. Especially not Cerise.' He kissed her lingeringly. 'And I know you feel far too sorry for Cerise ever to be jealous of her.'

'I do,' Cathy admitted. 'I feel very sorry for her.'

He held her close. 'It wouldn't have worked—Cerise's little scheme, I mean. No matter where you went, I'd have come looking for you and found you . . .'

His kiss was a deep caress that fulfilled even as it made her hunger for more. The summer sun flooded the room, and on the lawn outside, Ursula Hunniford squatted in front of a rose, lost in wonder at the intricacy of its petals, the brightness of its colours. Fabian stared into Cathy's eyes, the desire in him taut and full.

'So much has happened in such a short time. It's all almost too much to take in. It seems only days ago that you walked into my office with huge eyes and pale cheeks, asking me to get you out of trouble.'

'It's nearly four months,' she reminded him. Colour touched her throat and cheeks, and she dropped her long lashes.

'Will you ever understand—why I did that crazy thing?'

'I understood weeks ago,' he said gently. 'I understood that night at the window, when you told me all about Tim, and what had happened between you. There was never any doubt in my mind. And if there had been,' he smiled, 'Andrea Lorenz would have settled them that Sunday afternoon.'

'You discussed me? The two of you?' Cathy blinked in embarrassed confusion. 'Even about the photographs?'

'Andrea knew that I knew,' he nodded. 'There was no secret. She simply told me the psychological background to what you did. That going to *Caprice* was an irrational, crazy outburst that headed you away from a nervous collapse that might have been very serious indeed. Much more serious,' he smiled, 'than appearing in *Caprice* wearing nothing more than a red straw hat!'

'We'll make all our dreams come true,' he assured her meaningfully. 'But first there's something else.' The laughter faded from his eyes, and his face grew serious. 'My thanks.' He lifted her hand to his lips, his eyes deep and serious. 'Without you, my love, I'd never have come out of the darkness.'

'You're strong——' she smiled, but he shook his head.

'No. Your love is greater than my strength, Cathy. There are so many who need you to survive. Your father, the children at the Addington, Ursula, even my father. And now me.' His face blurred in her sight, but she gazed at him steadily, her lip trembling. 'And I need you most of all, Cathy. Don't ever leave me.'

'I won't.' She didn't need to promise. 'I'm yours for ever, Fabian.' He drew her into the warmth of his embrace, the heaven she had somehow won. 'For ever.' Her eyes were wet as she clung to him. 'For ever.'

Take 4
Exciting Books
Absolutely
FREE

Love, romance, intrigue... all are captured for you by
Mills & Boon's top-selling authors. By becoming a
regular reader of Mills & Boon's Romances you can
enjoy 6 superb new titles every month plus a whole
range of special benefits: your very own personal
membership card, a free monthly newsletter packed
with recipes, competitions, exclusive book offers and
a monthly guide to the stars, plus extra bargain offers
and big cash savings.

AND an Introductory FREE GIFT for YOU.
Turn over the page for details.

As a special introduction we will send you four exciting Mills & Boon Romances Free and without obligation when you complete and return this coupon.

At the same time we will reserve a subscription to Mills & Boon Reader Service for you. Every month, you will receive 6 of the very latest novels by leading Romantic Fiction authors, delivered direct to your door. You don't pay extra for delivery — postage and packing is always completely Free. There is no obligation or commitment — you can cancel your subscription at any time.

You have nothing to lose and a whole world of romance to gain.

Just fill in and post the coupon today to **MILLS & BOON READER SERVICE, FREEPOST, P.O. BOX 236, CROYDON, SURREY CR9 9EL.**

Please Note:- **READERS IN SOUTH AFRICA write to Mills & Boon, Postbag X3010, Randburg 2125, S. Africa.**

FREE BOOKS CERTIFICATE

To: Mills & Boon Reader Service, FREEPOST, P.O. Box 236, Croydon, Surrey CR9 9EL.

Please send me, free and without obligation, four Mills & Boon Romances, and reserve Reader Service Subscription for me. If I decide to subscribe I shall, from the beginning of th month following my free parcel of books, receive six new books each month for £6.60, po and packing free. If I decide not to subscribe, I shall write to you within 10 days. The fre books are mine to keep in any case. I understand that I may cancel my subscription at an time simply by writing to you. I am over 18 years of age.

Please write in BLOCK CAPITALS.

Signature _____

Name _____

Address _____

_____ Post code _____

SEND NO MONEY — TAKE NO RISKS.

Please don't forget to include your Postcode.

Remember, postcodes speed delivery. Offer applies in UK only and is not valid to present subscribers. Mills & Boon reserve the right to exercise discretion in granting membership. If price changes are necessary you will be notified.

6R *Offer expires June 30th 1985*